Contents

Introduction

■ ■ ■

Content Guidance

■ ■ ■

Questions and Answers

Introduction

About this guide

This unit guide is the third of a series covering the Edexcel specification for AS and A2 chemistry. It offers advice for the effective study of **Unit 3B: Laboratory Chemistry**.

The aim of this guide is to help you *understand* the chemistry — is it not intended as a shopping-list, enabling you to cram for an examination. The guide has three sections:

- **Introduction** — this provides guidance on study and revision, together with advice on approaches and techniques to ensure you answer the examination questions in the best way that you can. This section also contains guidance on how to write an experimental account.
- **Content Guidance** — this section is not intended to be a textbook. It offers guidelines on the main features of the content of Unit 3B, together with particular advice on making study more productive. However, because the information on error analysis and risk assessment that is desirable as background is not readily accessible (it is virtually absent from standard texts), these sections are more detailed. I have made clear where material is offered for information rather than as potentially examinable work.
- **Questions and Answers** — this shows you the sort of questions you can expect in the unit test. Answers are provided; in some cases, distinction is made between responses that might have been given by a grade-A candidate and those typical of a grade-C candidate. Careful consideration of these will improve your answers — but, much more importantly, will improve your understanding of the chemistry involved.

The effective understanding of chemistry requires time. No-one suggests it is an easy subject, but even those who find it difficult can overcome their problems by the proper investment of time.

To understand the chemistry, you have to make links between the various topics. The subject is coherent; it is not a collection of discrete modules. These links only come with experience, which means time spent thinking about chemistry, working with it and solving chemical problems. Time produces fluency with the ideas. If you have that, together with good technique, the examination will look after itself. Don't be an examination automaton — be a chemist.

Practical chemistry as a craft

Practical chemistry is to some extent a craft skill. Many people who find the conceptual parts of chemistry difficult can nonetheless be extremely good at volumetric analysis, because they work *carefully*. This unit guide is therefore different from the others in the series in that it offers advice on manipulative skills and has rather less theoretical chemistry. Manipulative skills are necessary for the practical assessment for which you actually *do* the experiments. They are also important in Unit 3B in which you can be asked about the reasons for doing particular things. Unlike the practical assessment, it is not an open-book examination. Careful attention to the principles behind practical work is essential preparation for Unit 3B.

Knowledge of the chemical reactions covered in Units 1 and 2 is also expected in Unit 3B; these are covered here in terms of what would be seen when these reactions are performed. For more details of the chemistry, you should refer to the appropriate unit guide books in this series, or elsewhere.

The specification

The specification states the chemistry that can be used in the unit tests and describes the format of those tests. This is not necessarily the same as what teachers might choose to teach or what you might choose to learn.

The purpose of this book is to help you with Unit 3B, but don't forget that what you are doing is learning *chemistry*. The specification can be obtained from Edexcel, either as a printed document or from the web at **http://www.edexcel.org.uk**.

The aims

The specification aims to:
- stimulate and sustain students' interest in, and enjoyment of, chemistry
- enable students to gain a knowledge and understanding of chemistry appropriate to these levels and to appreciate the interlinking patterns which are a distinguishing feature of the subject
- show the interrelationship between the development of the subject and its application (social, economic, environmental and technological) and recognise the value of chemistry to society and how it may be used responsibly
- develop skills in laboratory procedures and techniques, carry these out with due regard for safety and assess the uses and limitations of the procedures
- foster imaginative and critical thinking as well as the acquisition of knowledge, together with an appreciation of the intellectual discipline which the subject provides
- develop students' ability to acquire knowledge by means of practical work
- provide opportunities for students to bring together knowledge of how different areas of chemistry relate to each other
- provide an appropriate course for those who will end their study of the subject at one of these stages as well as laying a secure foundation for those who will continue their studies in this or related subjects

Writing the laboratory notebook

The skill of writing a laboratory notebook is a vital part of industrial and academic research.

The notebooks of Michael Faraday, handwritten with each experiment serially numbered, survive at the Royal Institution where he worked. They give in detail the design and execution of his experiments, with comment on their outcome and philosophical thoughts on their meaning. They have the essential feature that they enable his experiments to be repeated exactly as he did them. As a former Director of the Royal Institution pointed out, they are 'notebooks couched in plain language, with vivid phrases...'. It would be a brave professional scientist, let alone teacher or student, who would take issue with Faraday on this important point.

The widespread use of worksheets has tended to diminish the skills needed to write an experimental report properly. However, these skills are needed in Unit 3B, particularly in the section on planning experiments. You can write a coherent plan only if you have practised writing coherent accounts of your own experiments.

Plain language

The whole point of a laboratory notebook is that it should:
- say exactly what was done, and when
- make clear who did it
- enable someone else to do the same thing at some future date
- be durable and verifiable

Hardware

Books, pens and paper are the tools of your academic trade; skimping on them is absurd. Paper is made from spruce or larch trees grown for the purpose, not from rainforest timber — so don't be mean with it.

Here are some rules for hardware:
- Use hardback, bound notebooks — you can paste worksheets in where needed.
- Writing must be done in ink. Black is best. Blue ink fades more readily than black and red is least fade-proof of all. Some pens contain waterproof, fade-resistant inks and are made in many colours.
- Pencil should not be used for anything.

Organising your notebook

Anyone should be able to pick up your notebook and understand what you have written. This must be the main focus — you are writing for someone else. If the writing is clear to them, then it certainly will be to you. Achieving this requires some organisation as well as a certain style. The following points will help you to structure your notebook:

- Create a title page, stating your name, address (you might lose the book) and a brief indication of its purpose, for example 'Chemistry Practicals'.
- Follow the title page with a table of contents, allowing two pages so that you can list the experiments and find them easily when needed.
- Number the pages — this is tedious, but essential. Do it when the notebook is new.
- Abbreviations save time and effort. If you use them, include a table to explain them.
- Start each new piece of work on a fresh page.

Good notebook practice

The experimental introduction
The introduction to your experimental report should contain the following:
- the title of the experiment, which should also appear on any added pieces of paper (e.g. graphs) that are pasted into the notebook
- a statement of the problem or task, which is short and to the point (the elaboration of this comes later)
- the date. In industry or research, this is particularly important and may prove useful in your work too. Write the date unambiguously including the year — for example 2 July 2002. Do not write 2/7/2002, since those who use the American date system will think you mean 7 February.

The experimental plan
This is the part of the account that says what you are going to do. It may be that you have detailed instructions already, in which case they can be written or pasted into the notebook. If you are planning an investigation, you will have to write out your own plan.
- Use simple, direct statements or a bulleted or numbered list of instructions.
- Look forward to what you intend to *do* — do not repeat the introduction.
- Comment on any special features of the materials to be used. They may require special storage or handling, or there may be several varieties of the compound available, for example hydrated or anhydrous. Such factors are important and must be recorded.
- Safety! Part of chemical education is instruction in safe handling of potentially hazardous materials. There are some compounds that are not permitted in schools in the UK, mainly because they are carcinogenic or explosive. There are still plenty of hazards around and you should take these into account when planning the experiment. It could affect, for instance, the quantities you use or whether a fume cupboard is needed. *You* need to make a risk assessment. Standard practical exercises will have been assessed by teachers, but this does not remove the need for you to consider safety in your own experiments.

Observations and data
The observations you make and the data that you record will lead to the acceptance or rejection of your hypothesis and will decide what future experiments may be done. The observations and data are therefore central to the whole exercise.

- Observations and data must be recorded honestly.
- They should be recorded *as you make them*, in the notebook, in ink.
- Don't rely on memory, even for a minute or so. If someone distracts you, that particular piece of data may be forgotten. Also, you do not want your mind occupied with small details. You need to keep the overall experimental plan in mind.
- Don't use odd scraps of paper or the edge of your lab coat to record data.
- Raw data are precious — treat them with care.
- Data must be recorded as *completely* as possible. Don't worry too much about interpreting the data as you go along and don't worry if some of the observations appear banal. Omission of even the simplest things can dramatically affect the outcome of an experiment.
- Write carefully. Take care with numbers — never over-write; always cross out erroneous material with a single line and rewrite the correct data.
- Never use 'liquid paper' correction fluids.

Format

- Spread your work out.
- Tables must be written in vertical columns. Each column must be headed and the appropriate units should be included.
- Drawings need only illustrate novel apparatus — everyone knows what a beaker looks like. Don't try to draw a stopclock!
- Drawings should be sectional — don't draw the apparatus as you see it on the bench. There are examples on pages 26–30.
- Drawings should be large enough to allow labelling and should be simple and to the point.

Graphs

- Don't computer-plot your graphs. Graph plotting is an art — once you have learned it you can then decide whether or not to use machines and whether the graphs they plot are silly or useful. If you do eventually use a computer, use it to plot the points only. *You* must decide on the line.
- Each graph should have the experimental title and the date written clearly.
- Each axis must be labelled with the quantity and its unit, separated by a forward slash (e.g. time/s).
- Include error bars if you know the error limits.
- Give a clear table of the data you used to plot the graph.

Discussion and conclusion

- Write any calculations out clearly, showing all the steps and using units throughout.
- Relate your results to your hypothesis — do they support or refute it? Comparisons must be as quantitative as possible. A simple analysis practical will of course only produce a result.
- Record any ideas you have, however brief. If you do not write them down, you will forget them.

- Your conclusions should state:
  - what you found out
  - whether the hypothesis was supported or not, if appropriate
  - the error limits on your answer(s); a quantitative assessment of error should be made if possible, so that you can decide whether the use of a measuring cylinder rather than a pipette, say, really did make any meaningful difference to the result
  - suggestions for improvement in experimental design, if appropriate — the error analysis will be useful here
  - what to do next, if appropriate

Remember...
Science does not take place *on* the pages of textbooks or learned journals but it *is recorded* there. The quality of any work is only as good as the report that records it when the test tubes have long been washed up.

The unit test

The unit test consists of a structured question paper of 1 hour duration. It examines your ability to interpret information generated from or connected with experimental situations in the laboratory.

Questions may include:
- data for analysis — both quantitative and qualitative
- the opportunity to comment critically on information concerning experimental procedures
- revision of defective plans, including choice of apparatus or its assembly
- the understanding of the underlying principles of experiments
- calculations of reacting quantities and yields
- commenting on safety aspects, including risk assessment, from data supplied
- assessment of experimental error
- interpretation of the results of simple observation tests

The questions are in the context of the content of Units 1 and 2 and the content specified for Unit 3. They are weighted equally between the recall of knowledge and the application of knowledge.

The following command terms are used in the specification and in unit test questions. You must distinguish between them carefully.
- **Recall** — a simple remembering of facts learned, without any explanation or justification of these facts
- **Understand** — be able to explain the relationship between facts and underlying chemical principles (understanding enables you to use facts in new situations)
- **Predict** — say what you think will happen on the basis of learned principles
- **Define** — give a simple definition, without any explanation

- **Determine** — find out
- **Show** — relate one set of facts to another set
- **Interpret** — take data or other types of information and use them to construct chemical theories or principles
- **Describe** — state the characteristics of a particular material or thing
- **Explain** — use chemical theories or principles to say why a particular property of a substance or series of substances is as it is

Learning to learn

Learning is not instinctive — you have to develop suitable techniques to make your use of time effective. In particular, chemistry has peculiar difficulties that need to be understood if your studies are to be effective from the start.

Planning

Busy people do not achieve what they do by approaching their life haphazardly. They plan — so that if they are working they mean to be working, and if they are watching TV they have planned to do so. Planning is essential. You must know what you have to do each day and set aside time to do it. Furthermore, to devote time to study means you may have to give something up that you are already doing. There is no way that you can generate extra hours in the day.

Be realistic in your planning. You cannot work all the time, and you must build in time for recreation and family responsibilities.

Targets

When devising your plan, have a target for each study period. This might be a particular section of the specification, or it might be rearranging of information from text into pictures, or the construction of a flowchart relating all the reactions of group 1 and group 2 that you need to know. Whatever it is, be determined to master your target material before you leave it.

Reading chemistry textbooks

A page of chemistry has material of widely differing difficulty which requires different levels and styles of effort in order to master it. Therefore, the speed at which the various parts of a page can be read is variable. In addition, you should read with pencil and paper to hand and jot things down as you go, for example equations, diagrams and questions to be followed up. If you do not note the questions, you will forget them; if you do not master detail, you will never become fluent in chemistry.

Text

This is the easiest part to read, and little advice is needed here.

Chemical equations

Equations are used because they are quantitative, concise and internationally under-stood. Take time over them, copy them and check that they balance. Most of all, try to visualise what is happening as the reaction proceeds. If you can't, make a note to ask someone who can or — even better — ask your teacher to *show* you the reaction if at all possible. Equations describe real processes; they are not abstract algebraic constructs.

Graphs

Graphs give a lot of information, and they must be understood in detail rather than as a general impression. Take time over them. Note what the axes are, what the units are, the shape of the graph and what the shape means in chemical terms.

Tables

These are a means of displaying a lot of information. You need to be aware of the table headings and the units of numerical entries. Take time over them. What trends can be seen? How do these relate to chemical properties? Sometimes it can be useful to convert tables of data into graphs.

Diagrams

Diagrams of apparatus should be drawn in section. When you see them, copy them and ask yourself why the apparatus has the features it has. What is the difference between a distillation and a reflux apparatus, for example? When you do practical work, examine each piece of the apparatus closely so that you know both its form and function.

Mathematical equations

In chemistry, mathematical equations describe the real, physical world. If you do not understand what an equation means, ask someone who does.

Calculations

Do not take calculations on trust — work through them. First, make certain that you understand the problem, and then that you understand each step in the solution. Make clear the units of the physical quantities used and make sure you understand the underlying chemistry. If you have problems, ask.

Always make a note of problems and questions that you need to ask your teacher. Learning is not a contest or a trial. Nobody has ever learnt anything without effort or without running into difficulties from time to time — not even your teachers.

Notes

Most people have notes of some sort. Notes can take many forms: they might be permanent or temporary; they might be lists, diagrams or flowcharts. You have to develop your own styles — note the plural. For example, notes that are largely words can often be recast into charts or pictures and this is useful for imprinting the material. The more you rework the material, the clearer it will become.

Whatever form your notes take, they must be organised. Notes that are not indexed or filed properly are useless, as are notes written at enormous length and those written so cryptically that they are unintelligible a month later.

Writing

In chemistry, particularly in the early unit tests, extended writing is not often required. However, you need to be able to write concisely and accurately. This requires you to marshal your thoughts properly and needs to be practised during your ordinary learning.

Have your ideas assembled in your head before you start to write. You might imagine them as a list of bullet points. Before you write, have an idea of how you are going to link these points together and also how your answer will end. The space available for an answer is a poor guide to the amount that you have to write — handwriting sizes differ hugely, as does the ability to write crisply. Filling the space does not necessarily mean you have answered the question. The mark allocation suggests the number of points to be made, not the amount of writing needed.

Re-reading

When you have completed your work, you must re-read it critically. This is remarkably difficult, because you tend to read what you intended to write rather than what you actually did write. Nevertheless, time spent on the evaluation of your own work is time well spent. You should be able to eliminate at least the majority of silly errors — but you need to practise this in your ordinary work and not do it for the first time in an examination.

Approaching the unit test

The unit test is designed to allow you to show the examiner what you know. Answering questions successfully is not only a matter of knowing the chemistry but is also a matter of technique. Unit Test 3B is a paper with structured questions only, which are answered on the question paper.

Revision

- Start your revision in plenty of time. Make a list of the things that you need to do, emphasising the things that you find most difficult — and draw up a detailed revision plan. Work back from the examination date, ideally leaving an entire week free from fresh revision before that date. Be realistic in your revision plan and then add 25% to the timings because everything takes longer than you think.
- When revising, make a note of difficulties and ask your teacher about them. If you do not make these notes, you will forget to ask.
- Make use of past papers, but remember that these will have been written to a different specification.

- Revise ideas, rather than forms of words — you are after *understanding*.
- Scholarship requires time to be spent on the work.
- When you use the example questions in this book, make a determined effort to answer them before looking up the answers and comments.
- Remember that the answers here are not intended as model answers to be learnt parrot-fashion. They are answers designed to illuminate chemical ideas and understanding.

The exam

- *Read the question*. Questions usually change from one examination to the next. A question that looks the same, at a cursory glance, to one that you have seen before usually has significant differences when read carefully. Needless to say, candidates do not receive credit for writing answers to their own questions.
- Be aware of the number of marks available for a question. That is an excellent pointer to the number of things you need to say.
- Do not repeat the question in your answer. We can all see the question. The danger is that you then fill up the space available and think that you have answered the question, when in reality some or maybe all of the real points have been ignored.
- The name of a 'rule' is not an explanation for a chemical phenomenon. Thus, in equilibrium (Unit 2), a popular answer to a question on the effect of a change of pressure on an equilibrium system is 'Because of Le Chatelier's principle...'. That is simply a name for a rule — it does not explain anything.
- Even though all the questions in the unit test have to be answered, it is worth looking through the whole paper before you start to write. A great deal of subconscious thinking can be triggered, which will make things slightly easier when you do come to write. It's worth knowing what's around the corner.

Content
Guidance

This section is a guide to the content of **Unit 3B: Laboratory Chemistry**. It does not constitute a textbook for Unit 3B material.

The main areas of this unit are:
- Chemical tests
- Techniques used in volumetric analysis
- Enthalpy change measurements
- Techniques used in simple organic reactions
- Interpreting results
- Planning
- Estimating error
- Critical comment on experimental procedures
- Safety

For each part of the specification, you should also consult a standard textbook for more information. Chemistry is a subtle subject, and you need to have a good sense of where the information you are dealing with fits into the larger chemical landscape. This only comes by reading. Remember that the specification tells you only what can be examined in the unit test.

Chemical tests

Several reactions are given for each ion; not all would be suitable for a single test to show the presence of that ion. Sometimes with an analysis the nature of the substance becomes clear when the tests are considered as a whole.

Tests for simple ions

Chloride, Cl⁻

- AgCl, $PbCl_2$, Hg_2Cl_2 and CuCl are insoluble in water.
- Concentrated sulphuric acid liberates steamy acidic fumes of HCl from solid chlorides.

$$NaCl(s) + H_2SO_4(l) \longrightarrow NaHSO_4(s) + HCl(g)$$

- Addition of silver nitrate solution to a solution of a chloride that has been acidified with dilute nitric acid (test with blue litmus paper) gives a white precipitate of silver chloride.

$$Ag^+(aq) + Cl^-(aq) \longrightarrow AgCl(s)$$

The precipitate is readily soluble in dilute ammonia or in sodium thiosulphate solution.

$$AgCl(s) + 2NH_3(aq) \longrightarrow [Ag(NH_3)_2]^+(aq) + Cl^-(aq)$$
$$AgCl(s) + 2S_2O_3{}^{2-}(aq) \longrightarrow [Ag(S_2O_3)_2]^{3-}(aq) + Cl^-(aq)$$

Acidification with nitric acid is necessary to eliminate carbonate or sulphite, both of which interfere with the test by giving spurious precipitates. Concentrated solutions of sulphates can give a precipitate of silver sulphate in this test, but its appearance is wholly different from AgCl. The latter is truly white, whereas the sulphate is a pearly white, rather like opalescent nail varnish.

Bromide, Br⁻

- AgBr, $PbBr_2$, Hg_2Br_2 and CuBr are insoluble in water.
- Concentrated sulphuric acid gives a mixture of hydrogen bromide, bromine and sulphur dioxide with solid bromides. The HBr produced is oxidised by sulphuric acid. The mixture evolves steamy brownish acidic fumes.

$$NaBr(s) + H_2SO_4(l) \longrightarrow NaHSO_4(s) + HBr(g)$$
$$2HBr + H_2SO_4 \longrightarrow Br_2 + SO_2 + 2H_2O$$

Addition of silver nitrate solution to a solution of a bromide that has been acidified with dilute nitric acid (test with blue litmus paper) gives a cream precipitate of silver bromide.

$$Ag^+(aq) + Br^-(aq) \longrightarrow AgBr(s)$$

The precipitate is readily soluble in *concentrated* ammonia.

$$AgBr(s) + 2NH_3(aq) \longrightarrow [Ag(NH_3)_2]^+(aq) + Br^-(aq)$$

Acidification with nitric acid is necessary to eliminate carbonate or sulphite, both of which interfere with the test by giving spurious precipitates.

- Oxidising agents oxidise bromide to bromine, which is yellow or orange in aqueous solution. Bromine can be extracted from the solution by shaking with an immiscible organic solvent, for example hexane; the organic layer then turns orange. A suitable oxidising agent is sodium chlorate(I). This is added to the test solution, followed by a little dilute hydrochloric acid and a few cm^3 of hexane.

$$OCl^-(aq) + 2H^+(aq) + 2Br^-(aq) \longrightarrow Br_2(aq) + Cl^-(aq) + H_2O(l)$$

Iodide, I$^-$

- AgI, PbI$_2$, Hg$_2$I$_2$ and CuI are insoluble in water.
- Concentrated sulphuric acid gives a mixture of hydrogen iodide, iodine, hydrogen sulphide, sulphur and sulphur dioxide when added to solid iodides. The HI produced is oxidised by sulphuric acid. The mixture evolves purple acidic fumes and turns to a brown slurry.

$$NaI(s) + H_2SO_4(l) \longrightarrow NaHSO_4(s) + HI(g)$$
$$2HI + H_2SO_4 \longrightarrow I_2 + SO_2 + 2H_2O$$
$$6HI + H_2SO_4 \longrightarrow 3I_2 + S + 4H_2O$$
$$8HI + H_2SO_4 \longrightarrow 4I_2 + H_2S + 4H_2O$$

- Addition of silver nitrate solution to a solution of an iodide that has been acidified with dilute nitric acid (test with blue litmus paper) gives a yellow precipitate of silver iodide.

$$Ag^+(aq) + I^-(aq) \longrightarrow AgI(s)$$

The precipitate is insoluble even in concentrated ammonia. Acidification with nitric acid is necessary to eliminate carbonate or sulphite, both of which interfere with the test by giving spurious precipitates.

- Oxidising agents oxidise iodide to iodine, which is yellow or orange in aqueous solution. Iodine can be extracted from the solution by shaking with an immiscible organic solvent, for example hexane; the organic layer then turns purple. A suitable oxidising agent is sodium chlorate(I). This is added to the test solution, followed by a little dilute hydrochloric acid and a few cm^3 of hexane.

$$OCl^-(aq) + 2H^+(aq) + 2I^-(aq) \longrightarrow I_2(aq) + Cl^-(aq) + H_2O(l)$$

- Lead ethanoate or lead nitrate solutions give a bright yellow precipitate of lead(II) iodide with iodides.

$$Pb^{2+}(aq) + 2I^-(aq) \longrightarrow PbI_2(s)$$

- Solutions of copper(II) salts give a brown mixture containing iodine and copper(I) iodide when added to solutions of iodides.

$$2Cu^{2+}(aq) + 4I^-(aq) \longrightarrow 2CuI(s) + I_2(aq)$$

Addition of sodium thiosulphate solution decolorises the iodine, leaving pinkish-cream copper(I) iodide as a precipitate.

$$2S_2O_3^{2-}(aq) + I_2(aq) \longrightarrow 2I^-(aq) + S_4O_6^{2-}(aq)$$

Sulphite, SO$_3$$^{2-}$

- Sulphurous acid is considerably stronger than carbonic acid, so sulphites do not give the effervescence that is characteristic of carbonates when dilute acid is added.
- A sulphite on warming with dilute hydrochloric acid evolves sulphur dioxide. This turns acidified potassium dichromate(VI) solution (or paper) green.

$$SO_3^{2-}(aq) + 2H^+(aq) \longrightarrow H_2O(l) + SO_2(g)$$

- Barium chloride solution gives a white precipitate of barium sulphite.

$$SO_3^{2-}(aq) + Ba^{2+}(aq) \longrightarrow BaSO_3(s)$$

Addition of dilute hydrochloric acid causes the precipitate to dissolve without effervescence.

Sulphate, SO_4^{2-}

- $BaSO_4$, $SrSO_4$ and $PbSO_4$ are insoluble in water. $CaSO_4$ is sparingly soluble.
- Barium chloride solution added to the test solution acidified with dilute hydrochloric acid gives a white precipitate of barium sulphate.

$$Ba^{2+}(aq) + SO_4^{2-}(aq) \longrightarrow BaSO_4(s)$$

HSO_4^- reacts similarly with barium ions. However, these ions can be distinguished, since HSO_4^- solution is very acidic.

- Lead ethanoate solution gives a white precipitate of lead sulphate.

$$Pb^{2+}(aq) + SO_4^{2-}(aq) \longrightarrow PbSO_4(s)$$

Nitrate, NO_3^-

- All nitrates are water-soluble, so there is no precipitation reaction for this ion.
- Solid nitrates decompose on heating. Those of group 1 (except Li) give the nitrite and oxygen.

$$2NaNO_3(s) \longrightarrow 2NaNO_2(s) + O_2(g)$$

All others give the metal oxide, nitrogen dioxide, and oxygen. A brown gas is emitted that re-lights a glowing splint, owing to the presence of oxygen.

$$2Pb(NO_3)_2(s) \longrightarrow 2PbO(s) + O_2(g) + 2NO_2(g)$$

- Nitrate ions are reduced to ammonia by boiling with aluminium, or with Devarda's alloy, in sodium hydroxide solution. Devarda's alloy contains aluminium, zinc and copper. Since ammonium ions also give ammonia with NaOH, the test solution must be boiled with NaOH and the vapour tested for ammonia. If ammonia is present, heating must be continued until all the ammonia has gone. The mixture is then cooled, Devarda's alloy (or a piece of aluminium foil) is added and the mixture is reheated. A gas that turns moist red litmus paper blue indicates nitrate in the original solution.

$$3NO_3^-(aq) + 8Al(s) + 18H_2O(l) + 21OH^-(aq) \longrightarrow 8[Al(OH)_6]^{3-}(aq) + 3NH_3(g)$$

(This is not an equation to be remembered!)

Carbonate, CO_3^{2-}

- Only the alkali metal and ammonium carbonates are water-soluble. Some carbonates (e.g. zinc, copper(II)) are basic carbonates and contain a proportion of the hydroxide in their structure.
- Heating (at Bunsen temperatures) decomposes all but the alkali and alkaline earth metal carbonates, giving the oxide and carbon dioxide.

$$CuCO_3(s) \longrightarrow CuO(s) + CO_2(g)$$

- Dilute hydrochloric acid gives vigorous effervescence with carbonates, evolving carbon dioxide.

$$CO_3^{2-}(aq \text{ or } s) + 2H^+(aq) \longrightarrow H_2O(l) + CO_2(g)$$

The formation of carbon dioxide is shown by bubbling the gas evolved through limewater, which turns cloudy due to precipitation of calcium carbonate.

content guidance

Hydrogencarbonate (bicarbonate), HCO_3^-

- Only the alkali metal and ammonium hydrogencarbonates are obtainable as solids. Group 2 hydrogencarbonates exist only in solution. Other metals do not form hydrogencarbonates.
- Addition of calcium chloride solution to a hydrogencarbonate solution gives no precipitate, since calcium hydrogencarbonate is soluble. This distinguishes it from the carbonate, which does give a precipitate. On heating the calcium chloride/hydrogencarbonate mixture, a white precipitate appears because the hydrogencarbonate decomposes to carbonate.

$$Ca^{2+}(aq) + 2HCO_3^-(aq) \longrightarrow CaCO_3(s) + CO_2(g) + H_2O(l)$$

Sodium, Na^+

- A flame test gives a yellow-orange flame.
- There are no simple reagents that will precipitate sodium compounds.

Potassium, K^+

- A flame test gives a lilac flame. This is easily masked by sodium contamination. The yellow sodium light can be filtered out by looking at the flame through blue glass, in which case the potassium flame appears red.
- There are no simple reagents that will precipitate potassium compounds.

Magnesium, Mg^{2+}

- Sodium hydroxide solution precipitates white magnesium hydroxide, which is insoluble in excess NaOH.

$$Mg^{2+}(aq) + 2OH^-(aq) \longrightarrow Mg(OH)_2(s)$$

- Ammonia only partially precipitates magnesium hydroxide and not at all in the presence of ammonium ions. This is because magnesium hydroxide is fairly soluble and the small concentration of OH^- ions in ammonia becomes so low in the presence of ammonium ions that it is not sufficient to produce the precipitate.
- Sodium or potassium carbonate solution gives a white, gelatinous precipitate of the basic carbonate $Mg(OH)_2.4MgCO_3.5H_2O$.

Calcium, Ca^{2+}

- A flame test gives a reddish flame, which is often described as brick-red or orange-red.
- Dilute sulphuric acid gives a white precipitate of calcium sulphate if the original solution is fairly concentrated.

$$Ca^{2+}(aq) + SO_4^{2-}(aq) \longrightarrow CaSO_4(s)$$

- Sodium or potassium carbonate solutions precipitate white calcium carbonate.

$$Ca^{2+}(aq) + CO_3^{2-}(aq) \longrightarrow CaCO_3(s)$$

- Ammonium ethanedioate solution precipitates white calcium ethanedioate from neutral or alkaline solutions.

$$Ca^{2+}(aq) + C_2O_4^{2-}(aq) \longrightarrow CaC_2O_4(s)$$

The precipitate dissolves readily in dilute acid.

Ammonium, NH_4^+

- All ammonium salts decompose on heating. Ammonium nitrate may explode.

Ammonium chloride and sulphate give products that recombine on cooling, so that the salts apparently sublime.

$$NH_4NO_3(s) \longrightarrow N_2O(g) + 2H_2O(g)$$
$$NH_4Cl(s) \rightleftharpoons NH_3(g) + HCl(g)$$
$$(NH_4)_2SO_4(s) \rightleftharpoons 2NH_3(g) + SO_3(g) + H_2O(g)$$

Ammonium dichromate(VI) decomposes spectacularly on ignition in a reaction that involves oxidation of the cation by the anion. The initial orange solid gives a fluffy green product of much greater volume.

$$(NH_4)_2Cr_2O_7(s) \longrightarrow N_2(g) + Cr_2O_3(s) + 4H_2O(g)$$

- Alkalis (sodium hydroxide, calcium hydroxide) liberate ammonia from ammonium salts on warming with the solution, or even from a mixture of the solids. This is because hydroxide is a stronger base than ammonia, so it removes a hydrogen ion from the ammonium ion.

$$NH_4^+(aq) + OH^-(aq) \longrightarrow NH_3(g) + H_2O(l)$$

The test solution is warmed with sodium hydroxide solution and the vapour tested with moist red litmus paper. It is important to test the vapour immediately heating begins, since the ammonia is lost very quickly and by the time the solution boils it may well have all gone.

Barium, Ba^{2+}

- Barium sulphate and carbonate are insoluble. Soluble barium compounds are extremely poisonous.
- A flame test gives an apple-green flame.
- Addition of a soluble sulphate or hydrogen sulphate to a solution of barium ions gives a white precipitate of barium sulphate.

$$Ba^{2+}(aq) + SO_4^{2-}(aq) \longrightarrow BaSO_4(s)$$

Barium sulphate is insoluble in dilute hydrochloric acid.

- Sodium carbonate solution precipitates white barium carbonate.

$$Ba^{2+}(aq) + CO_3^{2-}(aq) \longrightarrow BaCO_3(s)$$

Barium carbonate dissolves with effervescence in dilute hydrochloric acid.

Chemical tests for gases

Hydrogen is colourless. If ignited, it burns with a squeaky pop. Igniting large quantities of hydrogen is dangerous. The reaction is:

$$2H_2(g) + O_2(g) \longrightarrow 2H_2O(g)$$

Hydrogen is an unlikely product in qualitative analysis. The only materials that give it are metals reacting with acid and ionic hydrides also reacting with acid. Ionic hydrides react explosively.

Oxygen is colourless. It relights a glowing splint. This is a good, simple example of the effect of an increase in concentration on the rate of a reaction.

Carbon dioxide is colourless. Bubbling it through limewater (a saturated solution of calcium hydroxide) gives a white (milky) precipitate of calcium carbonate.

$$Ca(OH)_2(aq) + CO_2(aq) \longrightarrow CaCO_3(s) + H_2O(l)$$

If carbon dioxide is blown through the milky suspension it gradually disappears, owing to formation of soluble calcium hydrogen carbonate.

$$CaCO_3(s) + CO_2(aq) + H_2O(l) \longrightarrow Ca(HCO_3)_2(aq)$$

If this solution is boiled, the reaction is reversed and the liquid becomes milky again.

Ammonia is colourless. It is the only common alkaline gas; it turns moist red litmus paper blue.

Chlorine is greenish yellow. It is a strong oxidising agent and this is the basis for the following tests:

- Chlorine bleaches moist red or blue litmus paper very quickly. Blue litmus may turn red *very* briefly at first.
- Chlorine turns moist starch-iodide paper black. The iodide ions are oxidised to iodine by chlorine and the iodine reacts with the starch to give the blue-black colour. (Bromine does the same, but is a brown gas; so does iodine, but the gas is purple.)
- Chlorine bubbled through a colourless solution of sodium bromide turns it yellow or orange, since bromine is liberated by oxidation of the bromide ion.

    $$Cl_2(aq) + 2Br^-(aq) \longrightarrow 2Cl^-(aq) + Br_2(aq)$$

- Chlorine bubbled through a colourless solution of sodium iodide turns it brown, possibly with a black precipitate if excess chlorine is used, since iodine is liberated by oxidation of the iodide ion.

    $$Cl_2(aq) + 3I^-(aq) \longrightarrow 2Cl^-(aq) + I_3^-(aq)$$

Iodine is formed initially. This reacts with excess iodide to produce the soluble brown I_3^- ion. If all the iodide ions are oxidised, the I_3^- ion cannot form and black solid iodine precipitates.

Nitrogen dioxide is brown. Unlike bromine, it neither bleaches litmus paper nor does it dissolve in organic solvents to give brown solutions. Holding a copper turning in the gas intensifies the brown colour.

Sulphur dioxide is colourless. It is a reducing agent and this is the chemical basis for the following tests:

- Sulphur dioxide turns an orange solution of potassium dichromate(VI) in sulphuric acid green (the colour of Cr^{3+} in aqueous solution).
- Sulphur dioxide turns a purple solution of potassium manganate(VII) in sulphuric acid colourless (the Mn^{2+} ion is actually pale pink, but far too pale to be seen in this test).

Techniques used in volumetric analysis

Volumetric analysis (titration) involves the reaction between two solutions. For one solution, both the volume and the concentration are known; for the other, the volume only is known. Apparatus used includes a burette, a pipette and a volumetric flask. Accurate results require careful technique.

The standard solution

The solution for which the concentration is accurately known is the **standard solution**. The concentration may have been found by a previous titration or by weighing the solute and making a solution of known volume. Such a solution is a **primary standard solution**.

Not all substances are suitable for use as primary standards. If a substance is to be weighed accurately enough for use in a standard solution, the following criteria must be met:
- the substance must be commercially available in a high state of purity or must be easily purified (e.g. by recrystallisation)
- the substance must not be volatile — if it is, some will be lost while it is being weighed
- the substance must not react with oxygen, carbon dioxide or water — if it does, then it cannot be weighed in air or dissolved in water

Suitable compounds for use as primary standards are:
- strong acid — sulphamic acid, NH_2SO_3H (a white solid)
- strong base — anhydrous sodium carbonate, Na_2CO_3 (a white solid)
- oxidising agent — potassium dichromate(VI), $K_2Cr_2O_7$ (a bright orange solid)
- reducing agent — ammonium iron(II) sulphate heptahydrate, $(NH_4)_2SO_4.FeSO_4.7H_2O$ (a pale green solid)

Preparing a standard solution

Weighing the solute accurately requires cleanliness and care. The guidelines below assume that you are using an electronic balance with a tare facility, i.e. where the reading can be made zero by pressing a button.
- Make sure the balance pan is clean and dry. Place the weighing bottle on the pan and tare the balance.
- Add a suitable amount of the solid to the bottle. Do this by taking the bottle off the pan and adding the solid away from the balance, so any spillage does not fall on the pan. For preference, avoid spillage!
- When you have the required amount, *write its value down immediately*. Do *not* write it on a scrap of paper!
- Transfer the solid to the graduated flask using a funnel. Wash out the weighing bottle into the funnel using a wash bottle and wash the remaining solid into the flask. Add about $50\,cm^3$ of distilled water and shake to dissolve.
- Some materials might have large crystals or may set solid when wetted. In these cases, the solid is transferred to a beaker, the weighing bottle washed into the beaker and about $50\,cm^3$ of distilled water added. The solution is stirred with a glass rod until the solid has dissolved. The solution is transferred completely to the graduated flask by pouring it down the same glass rod into a funnel and by washing any remaining solution off the beaker and the glass rod into the funnel.

- Whichever of the above methods is used, add distilled water so that the lower level of the meniscus is on the mark. Stopper the flask and mix *thoroughly* by inverting and shaking the flask vigorously five or six times. Simple shaking is not enough; most serious errors in volumetric analysis can be traced to poor mixing of the solution in the graduated flask.

Using the pipette

A glass bulb pipette will deliver the volume stated on it within acceptable limits only if it is used as its designer intended. The use of a pipette filler is obligatory — apart from hazards associated with getting some chemicals into your mouth, it avoids contamination of solutions with saliva. In safety questions in examinations, credit is not given for answers referring to the use of lab coats, safety glasses or pipette fillers, since all are assumed to be part of routine good practice.

- Using a pipette filler, draw a little of the solution into the pipette and use this to rinse the pipette. Discard these rinsings.
- Fill the pipette to about 2–3 cm above the mark. Pipette fillers are difficult to adjust accurately, so *quickly* remove the filler and close the pipette with your forefinger (not thumb). Release the solution until the bottom of the meniscus is on the mark.
- *Immediately* transfer the pipette to the conical flask in which you will do the titration, and allow the solution to dispense under gravity. Under no circumstances blow it out. Good analysis requires patience. When all the solution appears to have been dispensed, wait 15–20 seconds and dip the tip of the pipette under the surface of the liquid; then withdraw the pipette. It is calibrated to allow for the liquid remaining in the tip.

Using the burette

The burette will dispense solutions accurately only if used correctly.

- Making sure that the tap is shut, add about 10–15 cm^3 of the appropriate solution to the burette and rinse it out, not forgetting to open the tap and rinse the jet.
- Close the tap and fill the burette. A small funnel is helpful, but be careful not to overfill it — otherwise you'll be rinsing the outside of the burette as well. *Remove the funnel*, because titrating with a funnel in the burette can lead to serious error if a drop of liquid in the funnel stem falls into the burette during the titration.
- Bring the meniscus on to the scale by opening the tap over a suitable receptacle. There is no particular reason to bring the meniscus exactly to the zero mark.
- Make sure that the burette is *full to the tip of the jet*. Failure to ensure this is another source of serious error.
- Titration is a two-handed process. After a suitable indicator has been added to the solution in the conical flask, swirl the flask under the burette with your right hand whilst manipulating the burette tap with your left. Your thumb and forefinger should encircle the burette. This feels awkward at first but, after practice, becomes natural and gives good control of the tap.

- Add the titrant (the solution in the burette) slowly, swirling the flask all the time. As the endpoint is approached, the indicator will change colour more slowly. The titrant should be added drop by drop near to the endpoint — your aim is to make it change with the addition of one drop of titrant. Wait a few moments before reading the burette — this is to allow the solution time to drain down the walls of the burette.
- It is poor practice to run the titrant rapidly into the conical flask once you have an idea of the required volume. In some cases, particularly with titrations involving potassium manganate(VII), rapid addition can cause precipitation reactions that do not necessarily reverse when the solution is swirled.
- The titration is repeated until you have three *concordant* titres, i.e. volumes that are similar. This means within $0.2\,cm^3$ or better if you have been careful. Taking the mean of three titres that differ by $1\,cm^3$ or more is no guarantee of an accurate answer.

Enthalpy change measurements

The measurement of enthalpy of neutralisation

This technique can be used for any other type of reaction that can be carried out in an expanded polystyrene cup — so displacement reactions, for example between zinc and copper sulphate solution, can also be performed in this way.

The method of measuring the temperature change is designed to compensate for two sources of error: cooling (or sometimes warming, since some processes are endothermic and the temperature falls below room temperature) and slowness of reaction. The latter is not a problem in finding enthalpies of neutralisation, since all species are in solution. However, it can be a problem if the reaction is between a solution and a solid.

Using solutions of concentration around $2\,mol\,dm^{-3}$ will give a temperature rise of around $14\,°C$, which can be measured with reasonable accuracy.
- Measure $30\,cm^3$ of $2.00\,mol\,dm^{-3}$ hydrochloric acid into an *expanded* polystyrene cup.
- Measure the temperature of this solution every minute for 4 minutes.
- On the fifth minute add, with stirring, $30\,cm^3$ of $2.20\,mol\,dm^{-3}$ sodium hydroxide solution and measure the temperature every 30 s from $5\frac{1}{2}$ to 8 minutes.
- Plot a graph of temperature (*y*-axis) against time (*x*-axis).
- Extrapolate the lines on the graph to find the corrected temperature change at 5 minutes (see the answer to the examination question on page 45).

The heat change can then be calculated using $q = mc\Delta\theta$.

Techniques used in simple organic reactions

Heating under reflux

Many organic reactions are slow and require prolonged heating. To achieve this without loss of liquid, reaction mixtures are heated in a flask carrying a vertical condenser. This is heating under reflux; the solvent is condensed and returned to the flask, so the mixture can be heated for as long as desired.

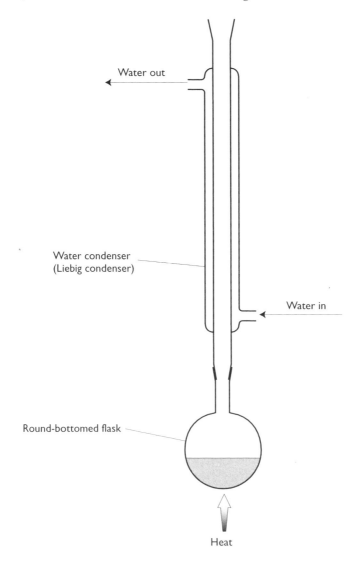

Water out

Water condenser
(Liebig condenser)

Water in

Round-bottomed flask

Heat

Simple distillation

Simple distillation is used where a volatile component has to be separated from a mixture, the other components of the mixture being very much less volatile (perhaps differing by 150 °C in boiling temperature) or non-volatile.

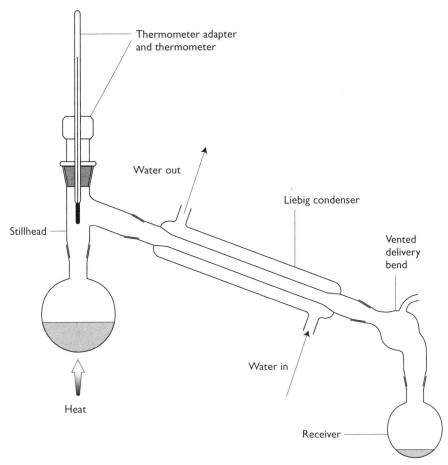

Fractional distillation

Fractional distillation is used to separate mixtures of volatile liquids.
- It is the first stage of petroleum refining. The fractions obtained are complex mixtures having a range of boiling temperatures. The process is continuous.
- It is used in organic preparations to separate perhaps two or three liquids, one or more of which can be obtained as a pure substance. The process is not continuous.

Drawing a diagram of an industrial fractionating column is wrong when dealing with the purification (sometimes known as the 'workup') of a laboratory-scale preparation.

The theoretical details of fractional distillation are not considered until the A2 course.

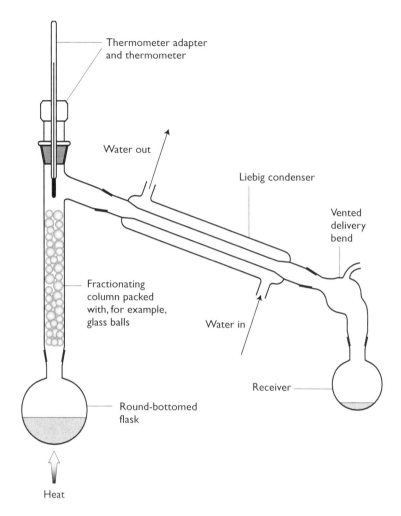

Thermometer adapter
and thermometer

Water out

Liebig condenser

Vented
delivery
bend

Fractionating
column packed
with, for example,
glass balls

Water in

Receiver

Round-bottomed
flask

Heat

Recrystallisation

Recrystallisation is used to purify a solid material by removing both soluble and insoluble impurities. The choice of solvent is important. The substance must be easily soluble in the boiling solvent and much less soluble at room temperature, or perhaps at 0 °C in an ice-water bath. This ensures the smallest possible loss of material, although some loss is inevitable with this technique. For a new compound, the choice of solvent will be a matter of trial and error.

- Dissolve the solid in the *minimum amount* of *boiling* solvent. This ensures that the solution is saturated with respect to the main solute but not with respect to the impurities, which are present in much smaller amounts.
- Filter the hot mixture through a preheated filter funnel. This removes insoluble impurities. The hot funnel is necessary to prevent the solute crystallising and blocking the funnel. Filtration under vacuum using a Buchner funnel is often preferred, because it is fast.

- Cool the hot filtrate, either to room temperature or, if necessary, in a bath of iced water or in a refrigerator. Rapid cooling gives small crystals, slow cooling large ones. The latter are aesthetically more attractive but are often less pure because big crystals can occlude impurities as they form slowly.
- Filter the cold mixture using a Buchner funnel.
- Wash the crystals with a *small* amount of *cold* solvent. This removes any impurity remaining on the surface of the crystals.
- Suck the crystals as dry as possible on the filter.
- Transfer the crystals to a desiccator to dry. Drying between filter paper is sometimes recommended, but it is a very poor method.

Melting point determination

The purity of a recrystallised solid is usually assessed by measuring its melting temperature (melting point). A pure solid melts sharply at a given temperature; impure solids melt at lower temperatures and also melt over a range of temperatures.

Melting temperatures can be found by using a large quantity of material and plotting a cooling curve. However, the usual method is to use melting point capillary tubes, which need only a few milligrams of the substance. Melting point tubes can be heated in paraffin oil or glycerol baths. Glycerol has the advantage that it is water-soluble and so the apparatus is easily washed, but it is more expensive than oil. Electrically heated metal blocks can also be used.

- Seal one end of a melting point capillary tube by placing it in the edge of a roaring Bunsen flame.
- When cold, press the open end gently into the crystals and then tap the sealed end gently on the bench. If the crystals are dry, it is not difficult to put crystals to a depth of about 5 mm in the tube in this manner.
- Attach the tube to a suitable thermometer, with a rubber band if using an oil bath, or place it in the heating block.
- Heat the bath or the block *slowly* and measure the temperature at which the solid melts. If heating is too rapid, the recorded temperature will be too high.

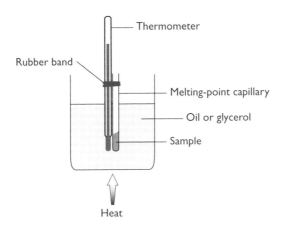

Boiling point determination

Boiling temperatures of liquids can be found either by heating them under reflux and measuring the temperature of the vapour, or by distillation. However, both these methods require quite large quantities of material. Siwoloboff's method can be used with about $2\,cm^3$ of liquid.

- Seal a melting point capillary tube as described above.
- Place the liquid whose boiling temperature is to be found in an ignition tube.
- Place the melting point capillary *open end downwards* in the liquid.
- Attach the ignition tube to a suitable thermometer and heat *slowly* in an oil bath.
- The boiling temperature of the liquid is reached when a *steady stream* of bubbles issues from the open end of the melting point capillary tube.

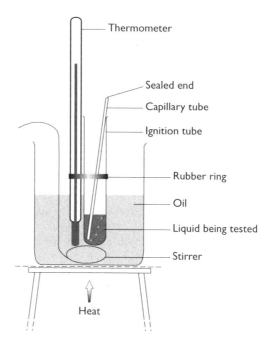

Knowing chemical reactions

You are expected to know the chemistry of the elements and compounds listed in Units 1 and 2 of the specification. You have to be able to recognise the results of reactions of these chemicals. You should know what you would *see* when these reactions are performed. This includes the chemistry of Groups 1, 2 and 7 and the chemistry associated with the alkanes, alkenes, halogenoalkanes and alcohols, as listed in Unit 2. This chemistry is covered in the Unit 1 and Unit 2 guides in this series, and elsewhere, so is not repeated here.

Interpreting results

The interpretation of results from experiments simply means that you have to learn to recognise the chemistry of compounds from both directions, as it were. Thus you should know what you see when you add sodium sulphate solution to a solution of barium chloride. Conversely, you should know that if you add barium chloride solution to another solution and get a white precipitate that is insoluble in hydrochloric acid, then the solution is a sulphate.

The interpretation of quantitative results depends on the context, but essentially it means that you should be able to calculate whatever it is that is being asked (titration calculations, or ones involving enthalpy changes), and also have some idea what the results mean.

The number of possible examples is very large, which is why this section stops here. The interpretation of results can only be achieved by practising interpretation during normal practical work. What you have to do when you make an observation is *always* to ask yourself what it means.

Planning

You can learn quite a lot about how experiments are planned by looking critically at the way in which practical instructions are given to you on worksheets or in practical books. Ask yourself in each case why the apparatus is as it is, what determines the order in which instructions are given and why particular analytical tests are appropriate. The following will help — but expertise in planning comes only from practice.

- Be clear about the nature of the problem. Many people cannot solve problems because they do not understand what the problem really is.
- Know the background theory.
- Be familiar with the techniques available that are appropriate to the problem. These could be techniques of organic preparation or qualitative analysis or measurement. If you do not know what tools are available, then you cannot do the job.
- Know the reactions in the specification. If you do not know what reactions are available, then you will not be able to plan, for example, a synthesis.
- In a quantitative experiment, be aware of the variables that could affect the measurements. In a kinetics experiment, these would be the concentration of the reactants, their surface area if solid, their pressure if gaseous and the temperature. Then make sure you know which variables have to be controlled (kept constant), so that you can measure the variable you are interested in.

Planning an experiment is a high-level skill, since it requires much background knowledge. The best approach in the early stages of your course is to look at practical instructions in the manner suggested above.

Estimating error

Experimental error: a fact of scientific life

Experimental error is always with us — it is in the nature of scientific measurement that *uncertainty* is associated with every quantitative result. This may be due to inherent limitations in the measuring equipment or techniques, or perhaps the experience and skill of the experimenter. However, mistakes do not count as part of experimental analysis, though it has to be said that some of the accounts given by students dwell too often on mistakes — blunders, let's not be coy — and too seldom on the *quantitative* assessment of error. It is easier to write about mistakes but it is not quantitative and does not present much of a test of the quality of the results.

This section is not intended as a course in statistics, so there is nothing concerning the analysis of large amounts of data. It is intended to help you assess error in a titration experiment or perhaps in results used to determine enthalpy of neutralisation.

The origin of experimental error

Errors — or uncertainties in experimental data — can arise in numerous ways. Their quantitative assessment is necessary because only then can a hypothesis be tested properly. The modern theory of atomic structure is believed because it *quantitatively* predicts all sorts of atomic properties. However, the experiments used to determine these properties were inevitably subject to uncertainty. Therefore, there have to be some criteria that can be used to decide whether two compared quantities are the same or not, or whether a particular reading truly belongs to a set of readings. The use of a number of titration results from a given analysis is an example of the latter.

Mistakes

Mistakes (I prefer the stronger word 'blunders'), such as failing to fill a burette to the jet or dropping some solid on the balance pan, are not errors in the sense meant in these pages. Unfortunately, many critiques of investigations written by students are fond of quoting blunders as a source of error, probably because they are easy to think of. However, they are neither quantitative nor helpful — experimental error in the true sense of uncertainty cannot be assessed if the experimenter was simply incompetent.

Human error

This is often confused with blunders, but is rather different, although no doubt one person's human error is another's blunder. It hinges on the experimenter doing the experiment to the best of their ability but being let down by inexperience. Such errors lessen with practice. They also do not help in the quantitative assessment of error.

Instrumental limitations

Uncertainties are inherent in any measuring instrument. A ruler, even if it is made as well as is technologically possible, has calibrations of finite width. A $25.0\,cm^3$ pipette of grade B accuracy delivers this volume to within $0.06\,cm^3$ if used correctly. A digital balance showing three decimal places can only weigh to within 0.0005 g by its very nature and even then only if it rounds the figures to those three places.

Calibrations are made under certain conditions, which have to be reproduced if the calibrations are to be true within the specified limits. For example, volumetric apparatus is usually calibrated at 20 °C, whereas the laboratory is usually at some other temperature.

Analogue devices, such as thermometers or burettes, often require the observer to interpolate between graduations on the scale. Some people will be better at this than others.

If you have a hot liquid and you need to measure its temperature, you will dip a thermometer into it. This will inevitably cool the liquid slightly. The amount of cooling is unlikely to be a source of major error, but it is present nevertheless.

These limitations exist. Whether they are dominant errors is another matter.

Observing the system may cause errors
The act of observation can cause serious errors in biological systems. For example, handling an animal causes adrenalin release that changes its biochemistry. The design of biological experiments is not our concern here but it is a particularly difficult aspect of experimental design. Chemistry is less susceptible, but you should be aware of the existence of the problem.

Errors due to external influences
Such errors may come from, for example, draughts on the balance pan (though this seems close to a blunder to me) or maybe from impurity in the chemicals used. Again, such things are unlikely to be significant in a carefully designed and executed experiment. However, because they are fairly obvious, they are often discussed by students.

Not all measurements have well-defined values
The temperature or the mass of a system has a particular value which, with suitable care, can be determined to acceptable degrees of uncertainty. Other properties do not — the diameter of a planet, although quoted in tables of data, is a mean value. The same is true for the thickness of a piece of paper or the diameter of a wire. These measurements will vary somewhat at different places. It is important to realise what sort of data you are dealing with.

Sampling
Many scientific measurements are made on populations. This is most obviously true in biology, but even the three values that you obtain from a titration is a population, albeit rather a small one. It is intuitively understood that the more samples you have from a given population, the less the error is likely to be. This is why I do not permit students to be satisfied with two congruent titration figures; I am slightly more convinced by three, and prefer four.

Related to this are errors arising from unrepresentative samples. Suppose that a chemist wishes to measure the levels of river pollution. The amount of a particular pollutant will depend on the time of day, the season of the year, and so on. So a measurement made at 3.00 p.m. on Friday may be unrepresentative of the mean levels of the pollutant during the rest of the week. It does not matter how many samples the researcher takes — if the sampling method is so biased, a true picture of the mean levels of pollutant in the river cannot be obtained. Therefore, a large population does not of itself ensure greater accuracy.

Combining errors in independent measurements

Many experiments depend on several measured quantities, each of which has an associated error. The rules for combining the errors are given below. *These will not be examined.* However, they can be used in your everyday work and will give you a feel for the magnitudes involved. More importantly, they will train you in the quantitative assessment of error.

In all the following cases, the two independent measurements A and B, with errors ΔA and ΔB, are combined to give the quantity X, which has the associated error ΔX.

Errors in sums or differences

The straightforward combination of individual errors in sums or differences gives an overall error that is too pessimistic. It is unlikely that the individual errors will both be in the same direction, though not of course impossible.

$$\text{If } X = A + B \text{ or } X = A - B, \text{ then: } \Delta X = \sqrt{(\Delta A)^2 + (\Delta B)^2}$$

This expression is the same whether the quantities are added or subtracted. If more than two quantities are involved, the expression is simply extended in a similar way.

$$\text{If } X = A + B - C, \text{ then: } \Delta X = \sqrt{(\Delta A)^2 + (\Delta B)^2 + (\Delta C)^2}$$

The resulting error is always larger than any of the individual errors, but not as large as their sum.

If two very similar values are subtracted, the resulting error can be very large. Such procedures are best avoided if at all possible (see Example 2, below).

Example 1

In an experiment to determine the enthalpy of neutralisation of sodium hydroxide by hydrochloric acid, the initial temperature was $19.2 \pm 0.2\,°C$ and the final temperature was $26.4 \pm 0.2\,°C$. What was the temperature rise?

$$\Delta T = (T_2 - T_1) \pm \Delta T$$
$$= (26.4 - 19.2) \pm \Delta T \,°C$$
$$= 7.2 \pm \Delta T \,°C$$

The error ΔT is given by

$$\Delta T = \sqrt{(\Delta T_1)^2 + (\Delta T_2)^2}$$
$$= \sqrt{(0.2\,°C)^2 + (0.2\,°C)^2}$$

$$= \sqrt{(0.08\,°C)^2} = 0.28\,°C$$

Thus: $\Delta T = 7.2 \pm 0.28\,°C$

This result would enable you to calculate the error in the value of the enthalpy of neutralisation.

Example 2
In an experiment to measure a quantity ΔQ, two values, $Q_1 = (90 \pm 2)$ and $Q_2 = (82 \pm 2)$, were obtained.

$$Q_1 - Q_2 = (90 - 82) \pm \Delta Q$$
$$\Delta Q = \sqrt{(\Delta Q_1)^2 + (\Delta Q_2)^2} = \sqrt{2^2 + 2^2} = \sqrt{8} = 2.8$$

Thus: $Q_1 - Q_2 = 8 \pm 2.8$

The error in each of the values of Q is about 2%; the error in their difference is 35%!

Errors in products or ratios
If $X = AB$ or $X = A/B$, then $\Delta X/X = \sqrt{(\Delta A/A)^2 + (\Delta B/B)^2}$

Notice that unlike the case of sums or differences above, we have to use *fractional* errors when dealing with products or ratios. If this is not done, then the units go badly awry — the fractional errors are numbers, not physical quantities. The quantities that are multiplied and divided are physical quantities and will not necessarily (or even usually) have the same units. By using fractional errors, the answer will have the correct units, because X (and its units) are in the denominator of the left-hand side of the expression.

Example
Tin reacts with iodine on heating under reflux in a perchoroethylene solvent to give an orange solid of formula SnI_x. In an experiment to find x, $(3.00 \pm 0.01)\,g$ of iodine was found to have reacted with $(0.70 \pm 0.01)\,g$ of tin. What is the value of x? (Molar masses: iodine atoms, $126.9\,g\,mol^{-1}$; tin, $118.7\,g\,mol^{-1}$)

'Amount' is used below in its technical chemical sense of 'number of moles'.

Amount of I atoms = mass of I/molar mass of I
$$= (3.00 \pm 0.01)\,g/126.9\,g\,mol^{-1}$$

Amount of Sn atoms = mass of Sn/molar mass of Sn
$$= (0.70 \pm 0.01)\,g/118.7\,g\,mol^{-1}$$

Therefore: $x = \dfrac{(3.00 \pm 0.01)\,g/126.9\,g\,mol^{-1}}{(0.70 \pm 0.01)\,g/118.7\,g\,mol^{-1}} \pm \Delta x$

$x = 4.01 \pm \Delta x$

The molar masses are constants, so it is necessary only to calculate the errors m_E in the mass of element E.

$$\Delta x/x = \sqrt{(\Delta m_1/m_1)^2 + (\Delta m_{Sn}/m_{Sn})^2}$$

$$= \sqrt{(0.01\,g/3.00\,g)^2 + (0.01\,g/0.70\,g)^2}$$

$$= \sqrt{(1.1 \times 10^{-5} + 2.0 \times 10^{-4})}$$

$$= \sqrt{(2.11 \times 10^{-4})} = 0.015$$

Therefore: $\Delta x = 0.015x = 0.015 \times 4 = 0.06$

Thus: $x = 4.01 \pm 0.06$

The fractional error in the mass of the tin is some ten times that of the iodine. This makes the error in the weighing of the tin dominant. In fact, the fractional error in the mass of the tin (0.014) is nearly the same as the fractional error in the value of x (0.015). If one fractional error is less than a third of another, the smaller one can usually be ignored.

Summary

- Errors should be quoted to two significant figures, at most. Errors are uncertainty limits and are statistical in nature.
- With sums or differences, ignore any error that is less than a third of the largest error.
- With products or ratios, ignore any *fractional* error that is less than one-third of the largest error.
- Find out what the dominant errors are likely to be in an experiment and concentrate on reducing those.
- If differences between two similar quantities are involved, take special care to reduce the error in those quantities as much as possible.
- If powers of quantities are to be taken, take special care to reduce the error in those quantities as much as possible.

Critical comment on experimental procedures

Many things have to be considered in a successful experimental design. The ability to detect bias or inbuilt inaccuracy or error in an experiment is an important part of scientific testing and is essential if the data or theory are to be trusted.

Below are some questions that you should ask of any experimental procedure. The appropriate ones to use will depend on whether you are talking about a preparation or qualitative or quantitative analysis. The questions will be asked for you in the examination — you would not be expected to formulate them for yourself. However, you should develop the habit of asking appropriately critical questions of every procedure that you undertake.

Detail

Is sufficient detail provided to enable the experiment to be repeated exactly?

Sometimes the answer to this is clear only if you try the experiment — not a possibility in the context of this unit test. You should be familiar enough with the experimental techniques covered in this unit to see when an experimental account is deficient in this respect.

Quantitative experiments

In quantitative experiments, have the quantities been calculated correctly and are they of a reasonable magnitude?

- In a preparation, is the scale on which it is planned appropriate for the purpose? The use of small quantities of starting material can often give no yield, simply because of the handling losses involved in the work-up of the reaction mixture. The use of too great a quantity may raise safety considerations or simply be too expensive for the purpose.
- Have the quantities of each reagent been calculated correctly? Thus, if a particular reagent has to be in excess (e.g. the reaction of hydrochloric acid with a marble chip, where the chip has to be completely dissolved and acid has to be left over for titration), the calculation may need to be checked.
- Are the concentrations of the solutions used in a titration reasonable? Use of very concentrated solutions (say 2.00 mol dm^{-3}) may give rise to inaccuracy, since one drop of the reagent contains quite a large amount of solute in terms of likely error in measurement of the solution volume. Use of very dilute solutions may give rise to large titres — not necessarily wrong, but certainly inconvenient if a burette has to be refilled.
- If limits have been set on the amount of material to be weighed out, have these limits been adhered to?

Apparatus

Is the apparatus used correct for the purpose?

- In preparative work, it is not correct to use fractional distillation when simple distillation will suffice.
- If a thermometer is used, check that the correct temperature range has been selected.
- In titrations, check that the apparatus used is appropriate to the purpose and to the accuracy required for the particular step. The measurement of 25.0 cm^3 of a solution requires a pipette or a burette; the measurement of 26.7 cm^3 of a solution requires a burette and not a pipette. The addition of sulphuric acid is required in some titrations, particularly those with potassium manganate(VII) and potassium dichromate(VI). This is to provide an acidic medium for the reaction, but the quantity of acid is not particularly critical and so the use of a measuring cylinder is sufficiently accurate in this case.

Data

Do the numerical data and the use made of them make sense?

- If the experiment is a titration, check for *concordant* titres, i.e. titres that are the same within reasonable error. Reasonable error may be $0.2\,cm^3$ for a straight-forward acid–base titration in the hands of a good analyst.
- Check that mean values have been calculated from individual values that are comparable. If they are not, look at the criteria used to select the values employed to calculate the mean.
- Do the lines drawn on graphs relate properly to the points and to the expected form of the data?
- Check that any numerical answer is quoted to a sensible number of significant figures, with appropriate units.
- Are all the necessary controls in place — is the experiment a 'fair test'?

Safety

Safety is important in chemistry for obvious reasons. Chemistry deals with compounds that may be hazardous, so part of a chemist's training is in the safe use of hazardous materials.

In any question on safety, you would be expected to suggest safety precautions specific to the experiment under consideration and to be able to assess which is the most significant of various hazards presented.

In this context, the use of lab coats, safety glasses and pipette fillers is considered routine good practice and does not receive credit in examination answers.

The following is presented to give you an idea of the basis on which risk assessments might be made. *Safety will not be examined in anything like this detail.* However, comments made by students on safety matters tend to be either so trivial as to be not worth reading or so apocalyptic as to suggest that all chemistry should cease forthwith. I hope this might help to correct the balance.

Whether a procedure is safe or not depends on:
- the intrinsic hazards presented by the chemicals used
- the scale on which the experiment is to be performed
- the containment regime used — for example, whether the experiment is to be done in an open laboratory or in a fume cupboard
- the time of exposure, though this does not affect the initial estimate of risk
- the skill and experience of the experimenter

Every experiment should be the subject of a risk assessment by the institution that intends to perform it. All of the above will contribute to the final assessment as to whether the risk presented is acceptable and whether the experiment is therefore feasible. The following is included to illustrate one particular approach, suggested by the Royal Society of Chemistry for use in schools.

Hazard evaluation

The **hazard** associated with a substance is its potential to impair health. Some degree of hazard can be ascribed to almost any substance, whilst for some, the toxicity or the harmful effects are not fully known.

Substances that are likely to be hazardous are those that are:
- very toxic (including carcinogenic materials)
- toxic
- harmful
- corrosive
- irritant

Hazardous substances also include those that:
- have a maximum exposure limit (MEL)
- have an occupational exposure standard (OES)
- may produce dusts in appreciable concentration (typically $10\,mg\,m^{-3}$ total inhalable dust)

Hazard categories are used to help the hazard evaluation:

Hazard category	Hazard classification
Extreme	(None kept in schools)
High	Very toxic; toxic; defined MEL or OES; substances with unknown toxicity
Medium	Harmful; irritant; corrosive
Low	Substances not meeting criteria for hazard labelling

Each substance to be used should be checked and its hazard category noted on the risk assessment sheet for the proposed experiment.

Exposure potential

Hazardous substances vary enormously in potency. A substance with a high hazard may present an acceptably small risk if the exposure potential is low. Conversely, unacceptable risks may result from high exposures to substances with low hazard.

Factors to be taken into account in evaluating exposure potential relate to both **substance** and **activity**.

Substance factors include:
- quantity used
- physical form and properties
- volatility

- dustiness
- concentration if in solution

Activity factors include:
- potential for exposure (e.g. production of aerosol)
- route of exposure (skin, inhalation, ingestion)
- frequency and duration of activity

Small-scale working is preferred wherever possible.

Typical basis for estimating exposure potential

The normal basis for estimating exposure potential is shown in the matrix below.

Score	1	10	100
(A) Quantity of substance	Less than 1 g	1–100 g	More than 100 g
(B) Physical character of substance	Dense solids; non-volatile liquids; no skin absorption	Dusty or lyophilised solids; volatile liquids; low skin absorption	Gases; highly volatile liquids; aerosols; solutions that promote skin absorption
(C) Characteristics of operation or activity	Predominantly enclosed system; low chance of mishap	Partially open system; low chance of mishap	No physical barrier; any operation where chance of mishap is medium or high

The exposure potential is estimated by multiplying A × B × C.

ABC < 1000 = *low* exposure potential
1000 < ABC < 10 000 = *medium* exposure potential
10 000 < ABC = *high* exposure potential

Time factors such as the frequency and duration of an activity should be considered. Short duration tasks involving a few seconds' exposure at infrequent intervals should not affect the initial estimate. Continuous operations on a daily basis would probably raise the estimate to the next higher category.

Risk assessment

The risk assessment is then made using the matrix below, where risk = hazard category × exposure potential. A containment regime is then devised.

Hazard category	Exposure potential		
	Low	Medium	High
Low	1	1	1
Medium	1	2	2
High	2	2/3	2/3

Risks presented by substances in the '*extreme* hazard category' are unsuited to this evaluation procedure and must be addressed on an individual basis. (They would automatically be unsuitable for use in schools.)

Containment regime
- Experiments with a risk assessment of 1 can be carried out on an open bench.
- Those with a risk assessment of 2 require a fume cupboard or other specially vented area.
- Those with a risk assessment of 3 need a special facility. This would not usually be available in schools, so experiments falling in this category could not be carried out.

The appropriate containment regime is then selected or the experiment modified until its risk is acceptable.

Perhaps one misunderstanding could be dispelled here. Benzene is carcinogenic and its use is not allowed in schools. This does *not* mean that aromatic compounds in general are carcinogenic: some are; far more are not. Many natural products and metabolic intermediates are aromatic compounds containing the benzene ring.

Flammable substances

The attentive reader may have noticed that the above deals with toxicity only. There is another risk that may be far more significant for short-term, small-scale experiments — flammability. Flammable substances must be kept away from naked flames. Any necessary heating must be with a hot water bath (not heated from underneath by a Bunsen burner!) or an electric heating mantle.

Common hazards in school chemistry

The following list is not exhaustive or definitive by any means.

Halogens are toxic and harmful by inhalation, although iodine is much less so than chlorine or bromine, because it is a solid. Chlorine and bromine must always be used in a fume cupboard. Liquid bromine causes serious ulcerating burns and must be handled with gloves, so is best left to demonstration experiments by the teacher.

Ammonia is toxic. Concentrated ammonia solutions should be handled in the fume cupboard.

Concentrated mineral acids are corrosive. If spilt on the hands, washing with plenty of water — *never* alkali, which is even more damaging — is usually enough, but advice must be sought. Acid in the eye requires *immediate, copious* irrigation and prompt professional medical attention.

Barium chloride solution and **chromates** and **dichromates** are extremely poisonous.

Sodium or **potassium hydroxide** or **concentrated ammonia** in the eye is *extremely serious* and must always receive professional and *immediate* medical attention, following copious irrigation of the eye. Sodium hydroxide and other alkali metal hydroxides are among the most damaging of all common substances to skin and other tissue. Treat them with respect.

Phenol is damaging to skin and should always be handled with gloves.

None of the above is intended to deter people from doing chemistry — it is intended to encourage safe working practice.

Questions
&
Answers

In this section of the guide, there are two sets of questions, consisting of past AS unit tests.

Do not treat the answers as model answers or as rubber-stamp responses to be reproduced without thought. The most important reason for studying chemistry is to *understand* it, not merely to repeat it parrot-fashion — you have to do more than simply aim for a good grade.

In some instances, the difference between an A-grade response and a C-grade response has been suggested. This is not always possible, since many of the questions are short and do not require extended writing.

I do not suggest that this section covers all the possible questions that could be asked on Unit Test 3B — examiners are more resourceful than that and practical observations offer a rich field. However, there are examples of questions on each topic of Unit 3B.

Examiner's comments
Candidate responses to long-answer questions are followed by examiner's comments, preceded by the icon 🖉. They are interspersed in the answers and indicate where credit is due. They also point out common errors that lower-grade answers are prone to show.

Unit Test 3B, June 2001

(1) In an experiment to find the enthalpy change when copper is displaced from a solution of copper ions, excess zinc was added to $50.0\,cm^3$ of $1.00\,mol\,dm^{-3}$ aqueous copper(II) sulphate in a plastic cup.

$$Zn(s) + Cu^{2+}(aq) \longrightarrow Zn^{2+}(aq) + Cu(s)$$

The temperature of the solution in the cup was measured every minute for 10 minutes, with the zinc being added after 3.5 minutes. The temperature readings are shown on the graph below.

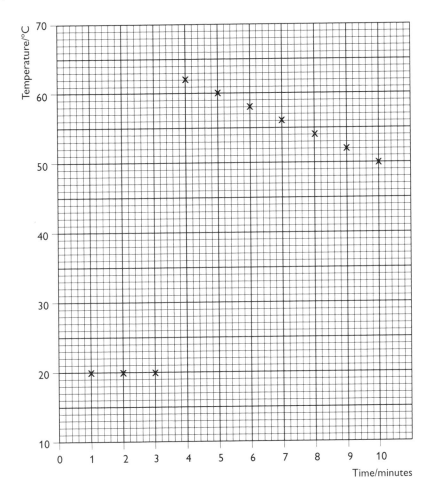

(a) Suggest two reasons why a series of temperature readings is taken rather than simply the initial and final readings. (2 marks)

(b) Use the graph to calculate the maximum temperature change, ΔT, as the reaction takes place. (2 marks)

(c) **Calculate the enthalpy change for the reaction using the formula below, giving your answer to an appropriate number of significant figures.**

$$\Delta H = -4.18 \times \Delta T \text{ kJ mol}^{-1}$$

(2 marks)

Total: 6 marks

Answer to Question 1

(a) This allows temperature fluctuations to be smoothed out/line of best fit to be drawn ✓; allows for loss of heat/accurate temperature change to be calculated ✓; allows for the reaction being slow/finite mixing time ✓.

📝 Any two of the three possible reasons would be credited.

(b)

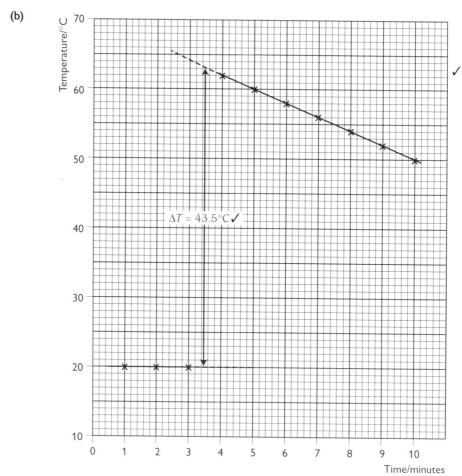

📝 There is 1 mark for correct extrapolation of lower and upper temperatures to get ΔT at 3.5 min and 1 mark for ΔT being correct to ± 1.0 °C, according to the candidate's method. This mark is consequential on a sensible method of finding the temperature change between 3 and 4 minutes. The commonest error in extrapolating is to run the line horizontally from the highest temperature on the graph; weaker candidates will do this, not appreciating the purpose of extrapolation.

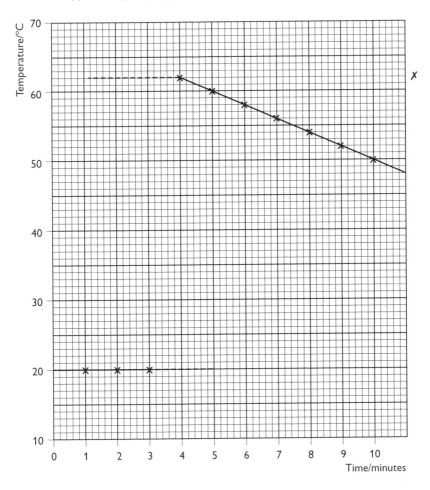

(c) $\Delta H = -181.8 \text{ kJ mol}^{-1}$

☑ There is 1 mark for ΔH correctly calculated from the ΔT value quoted in (b) with the correct sign, and 1 mark for the answer being quoted to 3 or 4 significant figures. If answers are quoted to 3 significant figures, they are safe from any penalty, provided that the question has not specified a different number of significant figures. If the question says 'to 2 significant figures', then no other number will score.

■ ▥ ▦

(2) 2-bromobutane was heated with excess aqueous potassium hydroxide until hydrolysis was complete. The resulting mixture was divided into two portions.

(a) When aqueous nitric acid followed by aqueous silver nitrate was added to one portion, a precipitate was formed.

(i) **Explain why aqueous nitric acid was added to the reaction mixture before aqueous silver nitrate.** (2 marks)

(ii) **Give the colour and the formula of the precipitate formed.** (2 marks)

(iii) **Suggest the effect of adding concentrated aqueous ammonia to the precipitate.** (1 mark)

(b) **The alcohol produced by the hydrolysis was separated from the second portion of the reaction mixture. Give the formula of a reagent which could be used to test for the presence of the –OH group in the alcohol. Describe the observation you would expect to make and give the formula of any one of the products of the test.** (3 marks)

Total: 8 marks

Answer to Question 2

(a) (i) To neutralise hydroxide ions/to make sure the solution is acidic ✓, otherwise silver nitrate will *react* with the alkali/to prevent the *formation* of spurious precipitates ✓.

All solutions that are tested for halide ions with silver nitrate are acidified with nitric acid. In this case, it is specifically for the removal of hydroxide ions which, if present, would give a brownish grey precipitate of silver oxide. It does not look anything like any silver halide, but would mask the formation of the precipitate you do want to see. I think that the best answer refers to OH^-. I would not like to see carbonate quoted, because although it is true that carbonate also interferes, it is obvious that it is not present in this case.

(ii) Cream/off white/*pale* yellow ✓; AgBr ✓

Describing colours can be a problem — stick to cream for AgBr.

(iii) The precipitate disappears/dissolves/a colourless solution is formed ✓.

Remember that dilute ammonia dissolves AgCl only and that any concentration of ammonia has no effect on AgI. The difference is a result of the differing solubility of the three halides and is easily understood using standard ideas of chemical equilibrium.

(b)

Reagent(s)	Observation	Product formula
PCl_5 ✓	Steamy fumes/misty fumes ✓	HCl/C_4H_9Cl /$POCl_3$ ✓
$K_2Cr_2O_7$ and H_2SO_4 ✓	Change from orange to green solution ✓ (both colours are needed)	$CH_3CH_2COCH_3/$ $Cr_2(SO_4)_3/K_2SO_4$ ✓
$KMnO_4$ and H_2SO_4 ✓	Change from purple to *colourless* solution ✓ (not 'clear'; both colours are needed)	$CH_3CH_2COCH_3/$ $MnSO_4/K_2SO_4$ ✓
Na ✓	Fizzing/bubbling ✓	C_4H_9ONa/H_2 ✓

A number of reagents can be used to show the presence of an alcohol. The table above shows four possible answers. The *formula* must be given — the name is not credited. The observation must relate to the reagent chosen; the product formulae can relate to the product from the reagent or the organic product. This is an excellent illustration of the notion that, if you have a free choice, you should choose the simplest. The use of PCl_5 gives the simplest answers as far as the product substances are concerned. Weaker scripts would probably get 1 or 2 out of the 3 possible marks, with the product formulae being the least likely to be right. Note that none of the above tests will demonstrate the presence of an alcohol if you are faced with a completely unknown substance — all of these reagents will react with other organic substances. However, given that the compound in the question is an alcohol, these tests do answer the question set.

■ ■ ■

(3) In an experiment to prepare cyclohexene, C_6H_{10}, concentrated sulphuric acid was added drop by drop to 6.00 g of cyclohexanol, $C_6H_{11}OH$, in the apparatus shown in the diagram below.

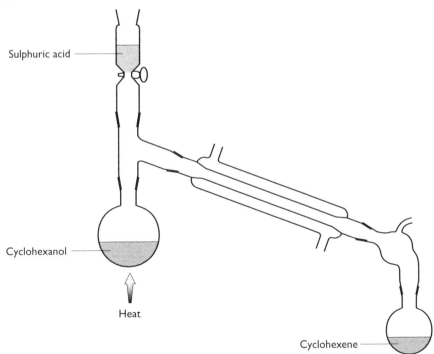

As the reaction took place, cyclohexene distilled over into the collection flask and a black deposit of carbon formed in the reaction flask.

The equation for the main reaction is:

$$C_6H_{11}OH(l) \longrightarrow C_6H_{10}(l) + H_2O(l)$$

After purification, 1.80 g of cyclohexene was collected.

(a) (i) **Calculate the amount (number of moles) of cyclohexanol used in the experiment.** (2 marks)

(ii) **Calculate the mass of cyclohexene that would be formed if all of the cyclohexanol was converted into cyclohexene.** (2 marks)

(iii) **Calculate the percentage yield of cyclohexene.** (1 mark)

(b) **Explain the relevance of the boiling points of cyclohexanol (161 °C) and cyclohexene (83.3 °C) to the success of the preparation.** (2 marks)

(c) **Explain why the formation of carbon reduces the yield of cyclohexene.** (1 mark)

(d) **Using the information below, suggest what precautions should be taken when clearing up the apparatus after the preparation:**

- **Sulphuric acid, H_2SO_4**
- **(Concentrated)**
- **Very corrosive — causes severe burns**
- **With water, heat is evolved**

(2 marks)

(e) **Suggest a reagent which could be used to test for the presence of the alkene double bond in cyclohexene. Give the expected result of the test.** (2 marks)

Total: 12 marks

Answer to Question 3

(a) (i) Molar mass of cyclohexanol = $(6 \times 12) + 11 + 16 + 1 = 100 \, g \, mol^{-1}$ ✓
Amount of cyclohexanol used = $6.0 \, g \div 100 \, g \, mol^{-1} = 0.06 \, mol$ ✓

🖉 The explicit writing-out of all the atomic masses to obtain the molar mass is not necessary to get the mark, but it is good practice. If the value of the molar mass is wrong, the absence of working means the examiner cannot tell whether the error is chemical or arithmetic. Such information makes no difference here, but could do so in a synoptic paper. Also, I have followed my own advice and included all the units, even though the mark scheme does not require this to gain the marks.

(ii) Molar mass of cyclohexene = $(6 \times 12) + 10 = 82 \, g \, mol^{-1}$
Amount of cyclohexene = $0.06 \, mol \times 82 \, g \, mol^{-1} = 4.92 \, g$ ✓

🖉 This part is marked consequentially on part (i), i.e. is the answer to part (i) $\times$ $82 \, g \, mol^{-1}$.

(iii) % yield = $(1.8 \, g \div 4.92 \, g) \times 100 = 36.6\%$ ✓

🖉 This is also consequential on the previous answer.

(b) The boiling temperature of cyclohexane is the lower ✓ of the two, so it distils off first ✓/the boiling temperature of cyclohexanol is the higher ✓ of the two, so it remains in the flask ✓.

🖉 As is usual, it is the *idea* that is being sought, so there are various forms of words that can be used.

(c) The carbon must come from the cyclohexanol and the carbon produced cannot be converted to cyclohexene ✓.

🗎 This is an example of a competing reaction. It occurs because concentrated sulphuric acid is an oxidising agent as well as a dehydrating agent, so it can remove hydrogen from the hydrocarbon, leaving carbon.

(d) The mixture should be added to water ✓ and not the other way round. Gloves should be worn ✓.

🗎 May her rest be long and placid
She added water to the acid
The other girl did what we taught her
And added acid to the water

(e)

Reagent(s)	Observation
Bromine water ✓	Yellow or orange solution goes colourless/is decolorised ✓
Potassium manganate(VII) and dilute sulphuric acid solution ✓	Purple solution goes colourless/is decolorised ✓
Potassium manganate(VII) and sodium carbonate/sodium hydroxide solution ✓	Purple solution gives brown precipitate ✓

🗎 Several reagents are possible — their formulae can be used. There is 1 mark for the reagent and 1 mark for the observation. Note that colour *changes* are necessary and that 'clear' does not mean 'colourless'.

■ ■ ■

(4) **A student carried out an experiment to find the percentage of calcium carbonate, $CaCO_3$, in a sample of limestone following his own plan. The student's account of the experiment, results, and calculations of the mean titre are given below.**

Account:
(A) Mass of piece of limestone = 5.24 g
(B) A measuring cylinder was used to transfer 50 cm³ of 2.00 mol dm⁻³ aqueous hydrochloric acid (an excess) to a 100 cm³ beaker. The piece of limestone was placed in the beaker and left there until there was no more effervescence.
$$CaCO_3(s) + 2HCl(aq) \longrightarrow CaCl_2(aq) + CO_2(g) + H_2O(l)$$
(C) The acidic solution in the beaker was filtered into a 250 cm³ volumetric flask. A small amount of solid impurity remained in the filter paper. The solution in the volumetric flask was carefully made up to 250 cm³ with distilled water.
(D) A pipette was used to transfer 25.0 cm³ portions of the acidic solution to conical flasks. The solution was then titrated with 0.100 mol dm⁻³ aqueous sodium hydroxide.
$$HCl(aq) + NaOH(aq) \longrightarrow NaCl(aq) + H_2O(l)$$

Results:

	1	2	3
Burette reading (final)	14.90	15.40	30.25
Burette reading (initial)	0.00	0.05	15.40
Titre/cm^3	14.90	15.35	14.85

$$\text{Mean titre} = \frac{14.90 + 15.35 + 14.85}{3} = 15.033 \text{ cm}^3$$

(a) The teacher judged the accuracy of the student's method to be poor. Suggestions made were that the procedure in (B) could be improved and that the titres used to calculate the mean were incorrectly chosen.

(i) Suggest, with a reason, *one* improvement to the student's procedure in (B). (2 marks)

(ii) Recalculate a value of the mean, making clear which titres you have chosen. Give your answer to an appropriate number of significant figures. (2 marks)

(b) (i) Using your answer to (a) (ii), calculate the amount (number of moles) of sodium hydroxide in the mean titre. (1 mark)

(ii) Hence, state the amount (number of moles) of hydrochloric acid in a 25.0 cm^3 portion of the acidic solution transferred in (D). (1 mark)

(iii) Hence, calculate the amount (number of moles) of hydrochloric acid remaining after the reaction in (B). (1 mark)

(iv) Calculate the number of moles of hydrochloric acid transferred to the beaker in (B). (1 mark)

(v) Hence, calculate the amount (number of moles) of hydrochloric acid used in the reaction in (B). (1 mark)

(vi) Hence, calculate the amount (number of moles) of calcium carbonate and the mass of calcium carbonate in the sample of limestone. (M_r of CaCO$_3$ = 100) (2 marks)

(vii) Hence, calculate the percentage of calcium carbonate by mass in the sample of limestone. (1 mark)

(c) The burette used in the titrations had an uncertainty for each reading of ± 0.05 cm^3.

(i) Which of the following should be regarded as the true value of the titre in titration 3?
- Between 14.80 cm^3 and 14.90 cm^3 (X)
- Between 14.825 cm^3 and 14.875 cm^3 (Y)
- Between 14.75 cm^3 and 14.95 cm^3 (Z) (1 mark)

(ii) Suggest *one* reason why a student may obtain volumes outside the uncertainty of the burette when carrying out a titration. (1 mark)

Total: 14 marks

Answer to Question 4

(a) (i)

Improvement	Reason
Use a pipette or burette instead of measuring cylinder ✓	Pipettes and burettes are more accurate ✓
Use a larger beaker or a conical flask ✓	Less chance of loss of solution by spray ✓
Powder the limestone/stir the mixture ✓	Makes the reaction faster ✓
Use more acid ✓	Gives a larger (and therefore more accurate) titre ✓

Possible answers are shown in the table above. There is 1 mark for the improvement and 1 mark for the reason. The improvement offered must apply to procedure B. The reason must match the improvement suggested. There are some subtle points here. A pipette or a burette is designed and calibrated to *deliver* the stated amount of solution; a measuring cylinder is designed to *contain* the stated amount. A 25 cm^3 pipette is accurate to about 0.25%, a measuring cylinder to about 1%. A standard method of reducing acid spray loss is to put a funnel in the mouth of a conical flask; the funnel is then washed off into the flask once reaction is complete. Limestone is a natural product and may not be homogeneous. Powdering it will ensure that any limestone surrounded (occluded) by unreactive impurity is available for reaction. Incidentally, traditional exercises of this sort have used pure, precipitated calcium carbonate rather than limestone, simply because the answer is then known. Exercises such as the one in the question give a 'context', but do not necessarily give a good estimate of the skill of the experimenter.

(ii) Choose titres 1 and 3 only ✓. The mean value is 14.875 cm^3 ✓.

Mean values of **14.88, 14.90** or **14.9 cm^3** are also acceptable. The choice of titres is obvious here. Less obvious in a real experiment might be the possibility that **15.35 cm^3** is not an outlier. I would need convincing with one or (better) two further titrations if I were standing in the laboratory criticising my students.

(b) (i) Amount of NaOH = 0.01488 dm^3 × 0.100 mol dm^{-3} ✓
$$= 0.001488 \, \text{mol}$$

This is consequential on the value of the mean quoted in (a) (ii). (Note that **14.88 cm^3** is **0.01488 dm^3**.)

(ii) Amount of HCl transferred = 0.001488 mol ✓

This is consequential on the answer to (b) (i).

(iii) Amount of HCl remaining after the reaction = 0.001488 mol × 10 = 0.01488 mol ✓

This is consequential on the answer to (b) (ii).

(iv) Amount of HCl transferred to the beaker $= 0.050\,dm^3 \times 2.00\,mol\,dm^{-3}$
$$= 0.100\,mol \checkmark$$

(v) Amount of HCl used = amount used originally – amount remaining
$$= (0.100 - 0.01488)\,mol = 0.08512\,mol \checkmark$$

📝 Consequentially, this is the answer to (b) (iv) minus the answer to (b) (iii).

(vi) $0.08512\,mol \div 2 = 0.0425\,mol$ of $CaCO_3$ ✓
Mass of $CaCO_3 = 0.0425\,mol \times 100\,g\,mol^{-1} = 4.25\,g$ ✓

📝 The division by 2 in the first step is because 2 moles of HCl react with each mole of $CaCO_3$.

(vii) % purity $= (4.25\,g \div 5.24\,g) \times 100 = 81.1\%$ ✓

📝 Remember that all working must be shown, so if you do not show it, you cannot get the credit.

(c) (i) Z ✓

📝 This answer is based simply on the maximum and minimum volumes obtainable by combining the burette readings and their errors, as shown below. The volumes are in cm^3.
    Maximum: 30.30 (highest) – 15.35 (lowest) = 14.95
    Minimum: 30.20 (lowest) – 15.45 (highest) = 14.75
This results in a pessimistic view of the errors. As stated in the error analysis part of this book, the likelihood of the error being the maximum (either way) in both the readings is small. A much more realistic view of the error limits where each reading is in error by $\pm 0.05\,cm^3$ is obtained from the error in the difference:
$$\sqrt{(0.05)^2 + (0.05)^2} = \pm 0.07\,cm^3$$
This puts the range at 14.78–14.92 cm^3. The answer is still Z.

(ii) Overshooting the endpoint/leaking tap/not reading the meniscus correctly/ burette not filled to the jet/funnel left in the top of the burette/burette not vertical.

📝 Any one of the above is acceptable for 1 mark.

■ ■ ■

(5) This is a planning exercise in which you are to describe a series of laboratory tests, the results of which will allow you to identify the five colourless aqueous solutions listed below:
- **ammonium sulphate, $(NH_4)_2SO_4$**
- **barium chloride, $BaCl_2$**
- **dilute hydrochloric acid, HCl**
- **sodium sulphate, Na_2SO_4**
- **sodium sulphite, Na_2SO_3**

The five solutions are in unlabelled bottles.

You are provided with aqueous sodium hydroxide, a book of red litmus paper, a supply of test tubes in racks, dropping pipettes and a **Bunsen burner** but with *no other reagents or apparatus.*

In your plan, you should make use of the tests described in the table below.

Ion	Test	Result
Ammonium ion, NH_4^+	Warm with aqueous sodium hydroxide	Alkaline gas evolved
Sulphate, SO_4^{2-}	Add aqueous barium chloride, $BaCl_2$, followed by dilute hydrochloric acid, HCl	White precipitate, insoluble in dilute hydrochloric acid, HCl
Sulphite, SO_3^{2-}	Add aqueous barium chloride, $BaCl_2$, followed by dilute hydrochloric acid, HCl	White precipitate, soluble in dilute hydrochloric acid, HCl; gas evolved as precipitate dissolves

In your plan, describe the sequence of tests, their expected results and your conclusions. Name any gases evolved in the tests. Make clear at which point you can identify a solution. There is no need to include quantities of solutions in your plan. (10 marks)

Total: 10 marks

Answer to Question 5

Add NaOH to each solution and warm ✓. Test the gases with damp red litmus, which turns blue with ammonium sulphate ✓. The gas is ammonia ✓.

Add ammonium sulphate to the remaining four solutions ✓. White precipitate forms with the solution of barium chloride ✓.

Add barium chloride to the remaining three solutions ✓. Two give white precipitates, sodium sulphate and sodium sulphite ✓. The remaining solution is HCl ✓.

Add HCl to the two white precipitates obtained above ✓. The one that dissolves is from sodium sulphite ✓. ✓

🖉 The scheme given above is not unique. There is 1 mark for the identification of ammonia and a maximum of 8 for the remaining test results and conclusions. The final mark is for the overall plan being logical and sensible. These are all standard tests, but the requirement for the tests to be applied logically is very important. The scheme *as a whole* has to work, for full credit.

Unit Test 3B, January 2002

(1) (a) The observations made when tests were carried out on a solid compound **X** are shown in the tables below. **X** contains one metal ion and one anion. Give the inferences that follow the observations by completing the statements in the tables.

(i) A flame test was carried out on **X**.

Observation	Inference
A lilac flame	The metal ion is…

(1 mark)

(ii) A sample of **X** was heated and the gas evolved tested.

Observation	Inferences
A gas is given off which relights a glowing splint	The gas is… X has the formula…

(2 marks)

(b) The observations made when tests were carried out on an aqueous solution **Y** are shown in the tables below. Give the inferences that follow the observations by completing the statements in the tables.

(i) Powdered sodium hydrogen carbonate was added to **Y** in a test tube. Any gas evolved was tested.

Observation	Inferences
Bubbles of gas evolved The gas turns limewater cloudy	The gas is… Y contains…ions

(2 marks)

(ii) A few drops of aqueous barium chloride followed by dilute hydrochloric acid were added to **Y**.

Observation	Inferences
White precipitate formed, which does not dissolve in dilute aqueous hydrochloric acid	The precipitate is… Y is aqueous…

(2 marks)

(c) The organic compound **Z** has the following structure:

$$CH_2 = CH - CH - CH_3$$
$$|$$
$$OH$$

Complete the table by writing the observations you would expect to make when the tests described are carried out.

Tests	Observations
Shake a few drops of Z with bromine solution	
Add phosphorus pentachloride to Z and test any gas evolved with damp blue litmus paper	
Add aqueous potassium dichromate(VI), acidified with aqueous sulphuric acid, to Z and heat the solution	

(6 marks)

Total: 13 marks

Answer to Question 1

(a) (i)

Observation	Inference
A lilac flame	The metal ion is potassium ✓

📝 No other ion gives this flame colour.

(ii)

Observation	Inferences
A gas is given off which relights a glowing splint	The gas is oxygen ✓ **X** has the formula KNO_2 ✓

📝 The salt is potassium nitrite. However, potassium nitrite is not the only salt that could give these reactions; potassium superoxide, KO_2, would, as would potassium manganate(VII). The specification makes clear that the tests are to be interpreted within the framework of the compounds met within the AS course, which is why the nitrite is given as the answer. The other compounds mentioned would also receive credit; however, the question does not specify that X is white or that the anion does not contain a metal.

(b) (i)

Observation	Inferences
Bubbles of gas evolved The gas turns limewater cloudy	The gas is carbon dioxide ✓ **Y** contains hydrogen (H^+) ions ✓

📝 An even better answer to the second part is H_3O^+ ions.

(ii)

Observation	Inferences
White precipitate formed, which does not dissolve in dilute aqueous hydrochloric acid	The precipitate is barium sulphate ✓ **Y** is aqueous sulphuric acid ✓

📝 As barium sulphate is formed, Y must be sulphuric acid.

(c)

Tests	Observations
Shake a few drops of Z with bromine solution	Yellow or orange ✓ solution is decolorised or becomes colourless ✓
Add phosphorus pentachloride to Z and test any gas evolved with damp blue litmus paper	Steamy fumes ✓; litmus paper turns red ✓
Add aqueous potassium dichromate(VI), acidified with aqueous sulphuric acid, to Z and heat the solution	The orange ✓ solution turns green ✓

📝 With bromine solution, it is necessary to give the colour *change* for full credit. This is frequently missed by weaker candidates. This reaction is the standard alkene test. Note that bromine water is not brown — *elemental* bromine is. With PCl_5, the fumes are of HCl and are not white; *misty* would be an equivalent description. The litmus paper shows the acidity of the fumes when dissolved in water, i.e. when HCl ionises. Dry HCl is not an acid and therefore dry litmus paper shows no change. With potassium dichromate(VI), the hydroxyl group is oxidised — the compound is a secondary alcohol. Note again that the colour *change* is needed for full credit. All the above are examples of interpretation of practical information.

■ ■ ■

(2) In a series of experiments to investigate the factors that control the rate of a chemical reaction, aqueous hydrochloric acid was added to calcium carbonate in a conical flask placed on an electronic balance.

$$CaCO_3(s) + 2HCl\ (aq) \longrightarrow CaCl_2(aq) + H_2O(l) + CO_2(aq)$$

The loss in mass of the flask and its contents was recorded for 15 minutes.

Four experiments were carried out. Experiments 1, 3 and 4 were carried out at room temperature (20 °C). The same mass of calcium carbonate (a large excess) was used in each experiment. The pieces of calcium carbonate were the same size in experiments 1, 2 and 4.

Experiment	Calcium carbonate	Hydrochloric acid
1	Small pieces	$50.0\ cm^3$ of $1.00\ mol\ dm^{-3}$
2	Small pieces	$50.0\ cm^3$ of $1.00\ mol\ dm^{-3}$, heated to 80 °C
3	One large piece	$50.0\ cm^3$ of $1.00\ mol\ dm^{-3}$
4	Small pieces	$50.0\ cm^3$ of $2.00\ mol\ dm^{-3}$

(a) The results of experiment 1 give the curve shown on the graph below.

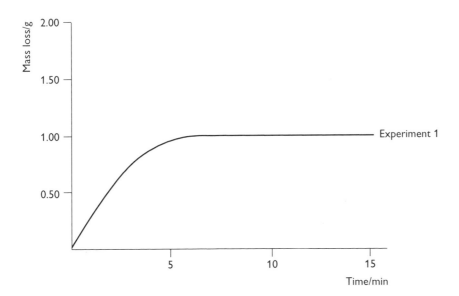

(i) **Explain why there is a loss of mass as the reaction proceeds.** (2 marks)
(ii) **Explain the shape of the curve drawn for experiment 1.** (2 marks)
(b) **Draw curves on the graph to represent the results you would expect for experiments 2, 3 and 4. Label the curves 2, 3 and 4.** (3 marks)
(c) (i) **Calculate the mass of calcium carbonate which exactly reacts with 50.0 cm³ of 1.00 mol dm⁻³ aqueous hydrochloric acid.**
    (Molar mass of $CaCO_3$ = 100 g mol⁻¹) (3 marks)
(ii) **Based on your answer to (c) (i), suggest a suitable mass of calcium carbonate to use in the experiments. Explain your answer.** (2 marks)

Total: 12 marks

Answer to Question 2

(a) (i) Carbon dioxide gas ✓ escapes from the flask ✓.

The comment that carbon dioxide is *gaseous* is critical to showing understanding for the first mark. If it were otherwise, then the products would simply remain in the flask and there would be no change in mass.

(ii) The reaction is initially fast and then slows ✓. The horizontal portion shows that the reaction has finished ✓.

This answer requires understanding of the *meaning* of the graph — that the slope of the graph at any point is a measure of the rate of the reaction and that the slope is greatest at first, becoming less and less until it is zero. This is because the hydrochloric acid is becoming less concentrated.

(b)

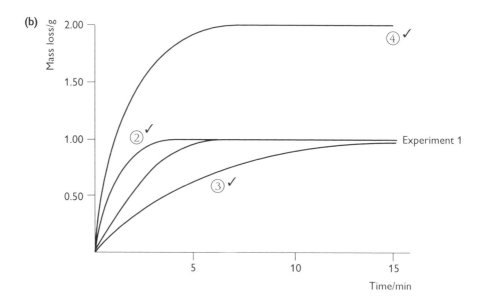

In experiment 2, the initial rate is greater because the temperature is higher and therefore there are more successful collisions between the hydrogen ions and the surface of the calcium carbonate. The amount of acid (which, remember, is all used up) is the same, so the mass loss is the same. In experiment 3, the surface area of the solid is smaller, so the collision frequency between the H^+ ions and the surface is smaller. The amount of acid is the same. In experiment 4, the more concentrated acid gives a faster reaction initially, and there is twice as much of it, so twice as much carbon dioxide is produced. This is why a large excess of calcium carbonate is specified. This is addressed more specifically in part (c) (ii) of this question. Comparing results between different experiments where solids react with solutions is, in practice, extremely difficult. The question says that the marble chips were the same size, but unless they are machined to be so, this is impossible to achieve. Even then, it is not necessarily the case that all would diminish in size in exactly the same way when attacked by the acid.

(c) (i) Amount of HCl = $0.050 \, dm^3 \times 1.00 \, mol \, dm^{-3} = 0.050 \, mol$ ✓
Amount of $CaCO_3$ reacted = $\frac{1}{2} \times 0.050 \, mol = 0.025 \, mol$ ✓
Mass of $CaCO_3$ reacted = $0.025 \, mol \times 100 \, g \, mol^{-1} = 2.5 \, g$ ✓

For full credit, the working must be shown. Simply writing 2.5 g as the answer will not get 3 marks. I have used the units throughout in the solution, because I believe that it makes things much clearer, a point already emphasised in the first book in this series. The mark scheme does not require that this should be done, but you should not be writing for the mark scheme alone.

(ii) More than 5 g ✓, because excess is needed and experiment 4 needs twice as much as all the others ✓.

☒ The mass should be at least twice that calculated in (c) (i). This means more than 5 g, or more than twice the answer given in (c) (i), because this section would be marked consequentially, provided that some explanation was given.

■ ■ ■

(3) The boiling temperature of 1-bromobutane is 102 °C. It can be prepared by the reaction shown by the equation below:

$$C_4H_9OH + NaBr + H_2SO_4 \longrightarrow C_4H_9Br + NaHSO_4 + H_2O$$

The preparation is in three stages:
- **Stage 1:** the reagents are heated for about 45 minutes in the apparatus shown in **Figure 1**.
- **Stage 2:** impure 1-bromobutane is extracted from the reaction mixture and transferred to the round-bottomed flask in the apparatus shown in **Figure 2**.
- **Stage 3:** a sample of pure 1-bromobutane is prepared using the apparatus shown in **Figure 2**. The sample is weighed and the yield calculated.

(a) **Give the names of the practical techniques carried out in each apparatus shown in Figures 1 and 2.** (2 marks)

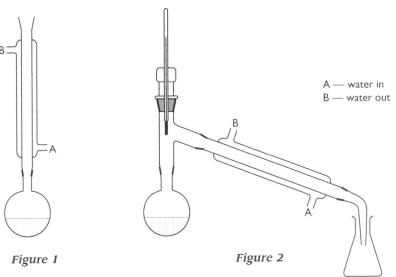

A — water in
B — water out

Figure 1   *Figure 2*

(b) (i) **Explain why, in Stage 1, the reactants are heated for such a long time.** (1 mark)

(ii) **Explain the purpose and the arrangement of the condenser in Figure 1.** (2 marks)

(c) **Briefly describe how you would use the apparatus shown in Figure 2 to give a sample of pure 1-bromobutane.** (3 marks)

(d) **A student preparing 1-bromobutane by this method calculated that the maximum yield in this preparation was 7.2 g. The actual yield was 3.1 g.**

(i) **Calculate the percentage yield.** (2 marks)

(ii) Suggest *two* reasons why the actual yield was much lower than the
maximum yield.

(2 marks)

Total: 12 marks

Answer to Question 3

(a) Figure 1 is for heating under reflux ✓. Figure 2 is for distillation ✓.

📝 In the past, Edexcel has not been keen on the use of 'reflux' as a verb, so the answer 'refluxing' is risky. It omits the heating, though it might be argued that reflux cannot occur in its absence. The answer given above is the best answer and cannot be faulted.

(b) (i) The reaction is slow ✓.

📝 Most organic syntheses are slow, because strong covalent bonds have to be broken.

(ii) It condenses reactant vapours and returns them to the flask ✓, which allows prolonged heating without loss of material ✓.

📝 The second point is important and is often missed by weaker candidates.

(c) Heat the mixture slowly ✓. Collect the fraction that boils ✓ at the stated boiling point of 1-bromobutane ✓.

📝 The slow heating is important and is a point often missed. Rapid heating can cause the temperature of the mixture to overshoot the thermometer reading considerably. Consequently, the vapours evolved will then be a mixture. Organic liquids have a much lower heat capacity than aqueous ones and need much gentler heating.

(d) (i) % yield = (3.1 g/7.2 g) × 100 ✓ = 43% ✓

📝 Since the calculation of yield follows on from cookery rather than quantitative analysis, 2 significant figures is a sensible accuracy to quote; 4 significant figures is not. As stated before, there is no *need* to include units — I just prefer it.

(ii) Incomplete reaction ✓ and handling losses ✓

📝 **Competing reactions** is another acceptable answer. In practice, all of these affect organic preparations.

■ ■ ■

(4) (a) In an experiment to standardise an aqueous solution of sodium hydroxide, 0.25 g of solid sulphamic acid, NH_2SO_3H, was dissolved in distilled water in a conical flask. When the aqueous sodium hydroxide was run into the flask from the burette, 23.45 cm^3 was required to exactly react with the sulphamic acid solution.

$$NH_2SO_3H(aq) + NaOH(aq) \longrightarrow NH_2SO_3Na(aq) + H_2O(l)$$

(i) Calculate the amount (number of moles) of sulphamic acid in 0.25 g.
(Molar mass of NH_2SO_3H is 97.0 g mol^{-1})

(1 mark)

(ii) **State the amount (number of moles) of sodium hydroxide in 23.45 cm³ of solution and hence calculate the concentration of the solution in mol dm⁻³.** (3 marks)

(b) **The balance used to weigh the sulphamic acid is accurate to ± 0.01 g. Calculate the percentage error in the mass of the sulphamic acid weighed.** (1 mark)

(c) **An alternative method to that described in (a) involves making an aqueous solution of sulphamic acid of *accurately known concentration*.**

Describe a procedure by which you would prepare 250 cm³ of aqueous sulphamic acid of accurately known concentration. Assume that you are provided with a weighing bottle containing between 2.40 g and 2.50 g of sulphamic acid and that this is a suitable mass to use.

In your answer, give full practical details, including the name of each piece of apparatus used, how each would be prepared for the procedure and how you would calculate the concentration (in mol dm⁻³) of the sulphamic acid solution. State, with a reason, one appropriate safety precaution that should be taken. (8 marks)

Total: 13 marks

Answer to Question 4

(a) (i) Amount of sulphamic acid = $0.25\,g \div 97\,g\,mol^{-1} = 2.58 \times 10^{-3}\,mol$ ✓

(ii) Amount of NaOH = $2.58 \times 10^{-3}\,mol$ ✓

Concentration of NaOH = $2.58 \times 10^{-3}\,mol \div 0.02345\,dm^3 = 0.110\,mol\,dm^{-3}$

🖰 The amount of NaOH would be marked consequentially from the answer to (a) (i). There is a 1:1 ratio between the acid and the base.

(b) % error = $(0.01\,g \div 0.25\,g) \times 100 = 4\%$ ✓

(c) Procedure:
- Rinse beaker/volumetric flask with pure water ✓
- Weigh bottle with sulphamic acid ✓
- Transfer sulphamic acid to beaker/volumetric flask ✓
- Reweigh empty bottle/wash bottle into beaker/volumetric flask ✓
- Dissolve sulphamic acid in a suitable volume of water in the beaker/volumetric flask ✓
- Transfer solution to volumetric flask (if a beaker was used) ✓
- Make to mark with pure water ✓
- Mix the solution thoroughly ✓

Concentration of the acid = (mass of sulphamic acid used $\div$ 97 g mol⁻¹) × 4 ✓
Safety precaution: wear gloves ✓

🖰 There are several acceptable ways of answering this question. There is a maximum of 6 marks for the procedure. In the calculation of sulphamic acid concentration, the multiplication by 4 is because the solution is made up to 250 cm³, but you want the amount in 1 dm³. Any safety comment appropriate to solutions of strong acids would score.